The Climate Debt

Combining the
Science, Politics
and Economics of
Climate Change

Other World Scientific Titles by the Author

The Entropy Crisis
ISBN: 978-981-277-968-7
ISBN: 978-981-277-969-4 (pbk)

Entropy and Sustainable Growth
ISBN: 978-981-3237-76-6
ISBN: 978-981-120-827-0 (pbk)

The Climate Debt

Combining the Science, Politics and Economics of Climate Change

Guy Deutscher

Tel Aviv University, Israel

NEW JERSEY · LONDON · SINGAPORE · BEIJING · SHANGHAI · HONG KONG · TAIPEI · CHENNAI · TOKYO

Published by

World Scientific Publishing Co. Pte. Ltd.

5 Toh Tuck Link, Singapore 596224

USA office: 27 Warren Street, Suite 401-402, Hackensack, NJ 07601

UK office: 57 Shelton Street, Covent Garden, London WC2H 9HE

Library of Congress Control Number: 2023939016

British Library Cataloguing-in-Publication Data
A catalogue record for this book is available from the British Library.

THE CLIMATE DEBT
Combining the Science, Politics and Economics of Climate Change

ISBN 978-981-127-400-8 (hardcover)
ISBN 978-981-127-591-3 (paperback)
ISBN 978-981-127-401-5 (ebook for institutions)
ISBN 978-981-127-402-2 (ebook for individuals)

For any available supplementary material, please visit
https://www.worldscientific.com/worldscibooks/10.1142/13344#t=suppl

Desk Editor: Joseph Ang

Typeset by Stallion Press
Email: enquiries@stallionpress.com

Printed in Singapore

Contents

Acknowledgments

I would like to dedicate this book to the memory of Maurice Allais. In the late 1990s, well before anyone else, he pointed out the dangers of generalized free trade that was promoted by the WTO and particularly by the European Union Maastricht Treaty. His opposition to the European Treaty was remarkable since he had been known as a strong supporter of a unified Europe and of a liberal economy, a support clearly expressed in his lectures at the Ecole des Mines de Paris that I attended as a student in the late 1950s. This surprising late opposition was largely ignored by official economic circles and did not get broad access to the media. His arguments were summarized in an authorized "*gedanken*" interview published in the review *Fakir No. 40, 2009*. Today they resonate strongly and are extensively quoted in this book.

Allais predicted that generalized free trade between countries characterized by very different levels of salaries would result in social misery in both developed and emerging economies. He was right. But he was not aware of the additional misery due to destruction of the environment that we are experiencing today caused by the same generalized free trade. This destruction and the resulting "climate debt" are the main theme of this book.

I would like to acknowledge an illuminating exchange with Erez Ben Zion and his archeology team at Tel Aviv University for making me aware of a well-documented and early example of such a destruction at the site commonly called "The Mines of King Solomon".

I am indebted to Jean Pierre Schwartz and Serge Binn for reading the manuscript and making valuable suggestions for improvements, and to Jean Poitou for his specific remarks on ice cap melting.

My thanks also to my wife Aline for her support: going over the manuscript with great care, pointing out inconsistencies and asking questions that have triggered further clarifications.

Introduction

People live better today than before the industrial revolution, in the countries where it has developed. This is what the proponents of progress say, and they protest against the prevailing pessimism precisely in those countries. Optimists have indeed no shortage of excellent arguments. We produce more while working less. Health, food security, access to water, education, paid vacations, secure retirement, and travel for all are now taken for granted. None of these existed 200 years ago at the dawn of the industrial revolution. Successive economic crises, more or less severe, have not so far called these rights into question — they have only been temporary.

But to what do we owe the benefits of what is commonly called progress? Did man suddenly become more intelligent two centuries ago, i.e. do we owe them essentially to the lightning progress of science and technology? Or to the consummate art of the economists who knew how to exploit these advances to benefit the greatest number? Or are these advances the result of social struggles led by the working classes in their confrontation with the capitalists?

As we know, success has many partners. Scientists, economists, and politicians have all contributed to it. But where does the pessimism expressed by some so vehemently come from?

Our thesis is that this pessimism is not a fad. To understand why it isn't, we must question the true origin of the progress made.

If we can produce more while working less — which has made social progress possible — it is because we have learned to exploit the resources offered by our planet much more efficiently. Coal, then oil, and gas have made it possible to replace human and animal labor with mechanization. It is the impact of this exploitation that is now the problem. In a little more than half a century, we have increased the concentration of greenhouse gases in the atmosphere by a good third. The consequences of this increase are now being felt. They are visible to everyone, and they generate fear.

Scientists and economists have each, in their own way, contributed to the efficient exploitation — some would say the plundering — of the treasures of our planet. They must now collaborate to limit the harmful consequences of this exploitation, to evaluate the damage caused, and to repair it as much as possible.

Chapter 1

Energy and Political Economy

The concept of political economy, i.e. economy in the modern sense, can be dated to the beginning of the 19th century with the publication of David Ricardo's book *On the Principles of Political Economy and Taxation* (19 April 1817). Trade plays an essential role in this book.

Before the beginning of the industrial era, the means of transport available severely limited long-distance trade. The conceptualization of the role that such exchanges could play in the development of society, a role that is central to Ricardo's theses, was therefore of little interest. Going back some 50,000 years, hunter-gatherers did not trade in staples. Bands lived mostly in isolation from each other. Homo Sapiens lived on what they could get locally and moved around when resources ran out. There was no exchange of goods, at most a few ornamental objects such as shells and pigments.

The hunter-gatherer lives from day to day and he does not transform anything. This changes completely with the development of agriculture at the end of the ice age 12,000 years ago. The climate then enters a long period of stability from which we benefit until today. Unlike the hunter-gatherer, the farmer must plan and store. He needs also to transform because the cereals are not directly edible as they are harvested, the wheat must first be ground before it can be made into bread.

Planning and transformation are still two fundamental characteristics of our modern societies. But there is a third one that was not yet wide-spread in the pre-industrial agricultural world, namely, exchange. The farmer lives essentially in autarky; he produces all he needs or almost all he needs (he also needs tools that he gets them from the blacksmith). This was the way of life of the vast majority of the population until the industrial revolution. The elites had only two ways to get rich, acquire land or gold. In this way of life, the economy had hardly any place, because the economy is the exchange, and this one was still very limited.

It is true that, thanks to the development of agriculture, humans had a more abundant and more predictable food supply than hunter-gatherers. This is what allowed the population to grow in a few thousand years from a few million individuals to a billion at the dawn of the industrial era, according to Malthus's estimate. But they did not have an important surplus or the means of transport which would have allowed long-distance exchanges. They could not move in large numbers into other industries. Malthus himself was opposed to such changes, fearing that a transfer of population from rural to urban concentrations would cause a decrease in agricultural production that could lead to famine.

1. Technology and Politics at the Time of King Solomon: Development of Copper Mines

The development of metallurgy, first that of bronze and then that of iron, profoundly modified the organization of society. Indeed, mining resources are often located far from agricultural areas of settlement. Their exploitation implied long-distance exchanges that were not previously practiced, such as the transport of ore from the mining site to the metal production site or the transport of food from the agricultural production areas to the exploitation site. They also needed energy for their high-temperature furnaces where the ore was transformed into metals.

A particularly important and interesting copper ore site is located in the Timna Valley, in an arid desert area northwest of the port of Eilat. The copper mines in this valley, commonly known as King Solomon's Mines, were exploited for hundreds of years from the 14th to the 9th century BCE. Mining began under Egyptian rule until the 12th century, but recent excavations have shown that the peak of activity was in the 10th century, during the reigns of King David and King Solomon. At that time, the Egyptians were no longer present.

One of the most important mining sites in the Timna Valley was discovered by Glueck (1935), at the top of a hill to which he gave the name "Slave Hill", mistaking the remains of a building for a detention center. In fact, a group of archaeologists led by Erez Ben Yosef from Tel Aviv University recently established that at this site the ore was processed and transformed into copper.

Climatic conditions have allowed the excellent preservation over more than 3,000 years of numerous traces of activity such as various artifacts, dyed textiles, remains of food, and especially animal excrement. Their analysis allowed archaeologists to date them precisely and to get an idea of the way of life of the men who worked on this hill (Erez Ben Yosef *et al.*, *Journal of Archeological Science* 11, 411 (2017)). The excavations revealed that functioning of the site was ensured by the long-distance transportation of necessary amenities.

It turns out that the building discovered by Glueck was not a detention center but a command post of what was an important industrial production site; its occupants were not slaves but highly skilled technician-founders, who constituted an elite with a high standard of living. This is evidenced by the presence of high-quality dyed textiles and well-preserved ornaments, as well as by the remains of abundant high-quality food. Cereal and fruit pollens, animal bones, and fish bones could not have been of local origin. The enclosure of the central building included stables, attested by the presence of a significant quantity of excrement. Their excellent preservation has allowed a detailed analysis which has shown that the animals, donkeys or mules, kept in these enclosures also benefited from a quality diet based on cereals (hay) and grape marc, which could not be of local origin either.

The surroundings are arid and desert-like. The absence of water does not allow the cultivation of cereals or vines. It does not allow the dyeing of textiles either. All these products therefore had to come from far away, more than 100 km from the mountains on the eastern bank of the Jordan (Edom) or more than 200 km from the Mediterranean coast. Researchers estimate that several hundred men worked at this site, with a similar number of draught animals transporting the goods and food they needed.

The so-called Slave Hill was thus the site of modern industrial activity. Bronze, made from copper, was still the most commonly used metal alloy in Solomon's time for the production of agricultural tools and weapons. Control of its production was of strategic importance. Copper ore is abundant in the Timna Valley, but its large-scale exploitation posed serious logistical problems because of its distance from the centers of political and economic power, as well as the valley's desert-like climatic conditions. The ore is mainly copper oxide. The method of its transformation into metallic copper, by reduction of the oxide with the help of carbon monoxide, CO, had already been known for a long time. But it was done on a small scale. During most of the Bronze Age, copper ore was not processed on site, but was transported further north where the necessary human (skilled workers) and material (wood and water) resources were available (see Figure 1).

The local production of copper allowed for a rationalization of the work, carried out by qualified personnel. However, local copper production posed difficult logistical problems. The local desert conditions did not allow for satisfactory living conditions for these personnel. Recent discoveries indicate that this was solved by long-distance trade, with draught animals bringing grain, fruit, and other quality foods to the production site and transporting the copper produced to where it was needed. In Timna, production was on a large scale, thanks to complex organization. It is in every respect a modern enterprise, of the same type as those that emerged at the time of the industrial revolution. It was this organization that allowed it to reach a high level of prosperity through the application of a technology already known, but practiced until then on a small scale.

The Old Testament describes a battle between King David's army against the Edomites in the Arabah Valley, not far from the Valley of Timna, and the establishment of a garrison. However, there is no archaeological evidence of a military presence of the armies of David and Solomon at the site of Timna. The region was populated by the Edomites, who had the know-how. They were probably the ones who exploited the site. But perhaps Solomon, renowned for his wisdom, found it more advantageous to make an agreement with them than to wage war against them? What one can say is that the existence of a strong central power, whatever it was, was necessary to ensure the security of a trade requiring long distance exchanges.

2. Energy Limits to Development: The Abandonment of Timna Mines

Archaeologists have established that the site of Timna was abandoned after several centuries of exploitation, shortly after it had reached its peak. The reasons for this abandonment are not obvious. The valley was still rich in ore. There are no traces of violence or destruction. Why did the beautiful organization that had achieved such prosperity suddenly stop working?

Two sources of energy were needed for copper production at Timna: food for the men and their draught animals, and fuel for their own needs (cooking) and for heating the furnaces. The food problem had been solved by long-distance transport that provided the necessary supplements.

But the wood used was of local origin, as shown by the analysis of charcoal remains found on the site. Wood transport over long distances would probably have been too costly. It was initially available locally in sufficient quantities, but the analysis of the charcoal remains have shown that the wood used was of increasingly distant origin.

Researchers have proposed that copper production stopped due to a lack of the fuel used in furnaces for smelting the ore and for copper production. This is not the only example of decadence. Others are more famous, like the cessation of activity in the great sites of the Inca civilization. But this one is particularly interesting thanks to the conservation over more than 3,000 years of organic waste whose analysis was so fruitful to reveal the detailed functioning of this site of industrial production. Its evolution could thus be traced in detail with precise dating. The fact that wood had to be fetched further and further away, making it increasingly expensive, shows that it was becoming scarce. There is therefore nothing mysterious about the cessation of production. High caloric quality wood from acacia trees and white broom bushes, available locally, had first been used. To explain the amount of slash found at the smelting sites, corresponding to the production of hundreds of tons of copper, thousands of acacia trees must have been uprooted. Once they became unavailable, other trees such as date trees had to be brought from more distant locations. Eventually, copper production ceased and the site was no longer occupied for a thousand years.

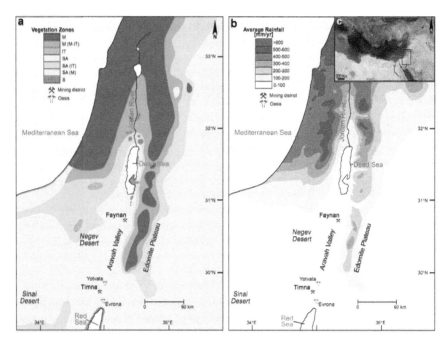

Figure 1.   a) The site of Timna, often called King Solomon copper mines, is located near the Red Sea in an arid isolated area, about 100 km from the relatively fertile Edomite Plateau and 200 km from the Mediterranean coast. Food for workers and copper production had to be transported over long distances. Copper production, after reaching a peak in the 10th century BCE, stopped abruptly. b) According to archeologists, this was likely due to the lack of fuel due to exhaustion of the limited local wood resources. (Maps from Mark Cavanagh, Erez Ben Yosef and Dafna Langgut, Science Reports 2022, 12: 15434).

This may therefore be the first historical example of an energy crisis. Its course is reminiscent of the Club of Rome model, according to which industrial production collapses when half of the natural resources in raw materials (in this case wood) have been exploited, because of their increasing cost. The result of this modeling is not intuitive. It is a sudden collapse, not a gradual decrease in production. There is no warning. Production continues to increase steadily before collapsing all at once.

It is tempting to hypothesize that this is precisely what happened 3,000 years ago in the Timna Valley. Copper production had increased there thanks to its rationalization, and with it prosperity and the consumption of wood. Progress continued as long as there was fuel nearby. Then, everything stopped.

In this arid region, deforestation is irreversible: forests do not grow back. Industrialization and the destruction of the environment were irreparable.

The history of King Solomon's Mines, as reconstructed by archaeologists after 3,000 years, could be considered a salutary lesson. It shows how the mastery of a technology associated with natural resources and exchanges that allow their accelerated exploitation can in the medium term lead to prosperity. The means implemented then were of course derisory compared to those we have today. The tools were primitive, the ovens rudimentary, and the goods were transported on donkeys with limited radius. Solomon's kingdom was little compared to a modern state. But the combination of methods used during his reign, if not directly under his control, to make the Timna Valley a major center of copper production was surprisingly modern. Unfortunately, it is perhaps the effectiveness of this combination that *ultimately* led to the collapse of production through the depletion of energy resources, and the destruction of a fragile environment.

3. Birth of the Industrial Society Through Coal Mining: A World Without Limits

Six thousand years ago, men had shown extraordinary ingenuity in finding a way to transform copper ore into metal. Three thousand years later, copper production reached its peak in Timna Valley. But the embryo of modern economy that developed at the time of King Solomon could not be generalized because the means of production were limited by the amount of work that men and their draft animals could provide, as well as by the fact that the only available fuel was wood.

Almost 3,000 years separate the climax of this episode and the dawn of the industrial revolution. During this long interval, there were no major advances in the production of metals.

The basic metallurgy of iron was already known 3,000 years ago, but its development was hampered by the lack of adequate fuel to reach the high temperatures it requires. The principle of iron metallurgy is the same as that of copper; in both cases the ore is an oxide or a combination of oxides that is reduced by exposing it to carbon monoxide at high temperatures. But the melting temperature of iron and its alloys is much higher than that of copper. The melting and reduction operation must be done at 1,500 versus 1,000 degrees. Obtaining high temperatures is easier with coal than with charcoal.

Unfortunately coal, unlike wood, is usually found deep in the earth rather than on the surface. To extract it, mines must be dug. But then there is the problem of water runoff, the evacuation of which requires the use of pumps, which need mechanical energy to be operated. The only mechanical energy available was provided by draught animals. It was limited and not sufficient to pump water from deep in the ground. It is this limit that was lifted in England with the invention of the steam engine. The work done by these machines allowed the pumping of water from great depths. This invention triggered the industrial revolution. Let's retrace some of its essential pages.

A first decisive step was taken by Thomas Savery in 1698. He showed that a drop in pressure occurs when steam is introduced and then cools down into a chamber previously at atmospheric pressure, and that this drop in pressure allows a lever system to exert a force that activates a water pump. This machine transformed heat — in this case the heat used to obtain steam — into mechanical energy that could be used to perform work, in this case the pumping of water. This machine was weak and inefficient; it could not pump water from great depths and its impact was very limited. But it was a revolution because, in spite of its weak pumping capabilities, it provided access to more coal than was needed to power it.

The next step was taken by Watts in 1765. In Savery's machine, the steam is introduced into an enclosure which is alternately a hot source when the steam is introduced and a cold source when it is cooled. In Watts's machine, the hot source and the cold source — the condenser — are separated. By this separation, the temperature difference between the two sources could be increased, and thus the efficiency of the machine, as Sadi Carnot later demonstrated.

In partnership with Roebuck and later with Boulton, Watts transformed his principled design in stages into a commercial machine that was available in 1776. Boulton, an entrepreneurial genius, realized that Watts's machine had a much wider application than pumping water in coal mines. He encouraged Watts to modify it so that it could be used as a motive force in all kinds of factories. This involved transforming the linear motion of the piston into a circular motion. This was accomplished in 1782, when Watts's machine replaced the work of 12 horses in a carpentry shop. By 1800, the machine was already in use in hundreds of spinning and flour mills.

Coal production in England increased exponentially. It went from 6 million tons in 1770 to 16 million tons in 1815 and 30 million tons in 1830, doubling roughly every 15 years. After revolutionizing the textile industry, the use of Watts's engine extended to land transportation. The first line using the steam locomotive was inaugurated in 1825 (Stockton to Darlington) for passenger transport. At the same time, steamship transportation was developed. The first steam crossing of the Atlantic took place in 1827 and by 1838 regular transatlantic connections were available.

Thanks to Savery's invention and the improvements made to it, coal resources had become virtually infinite: the steam engine could extract much more coal than it used for its operation. Large-scale production of iron and its alloys became possible. Its use became widespread in maritime construction and, as the name suggests, in railroads.

The next step was the use of coal for the production of electricity. The first coal-fired power plant dates from 1878 (7 kW, Saint Moritz). Edison's in 1882 provided lighting around Wall Street. Watts's machine was replaced by the steam turbine in 1884 (Sir Charles Parsons). In a few years, the power of the power plants increased from 7.5 kW to 50,000 kW, and today it reaches 1,000 MW.

At its peak, British coal production reached 250 million tons in 1920. World production reached nearly 8,000 million tons in 2013. It has multiplied by a factor of 1,000 since the beginning of the industrial era, roughly doubling every 30 years.

4. Economic and Political Exchanges

The rapid development of available energy led to an increase in the production of manufactured goods, and extended their long-distance exchange on a global scale. This was made possible by steamships, which reduced the cost of transport considerably compared to sailing. It is indeed faster and employs fewer sailors. Foreign trade then became an essential element of the economy, which thus became a political economy, that of David Ricardo. We shall return to this at length in Chapter 3.

The history of King Solomon's mines of 3,000 years ago, as reconstructed by archaeologists, can be considered an embryonic example of the industrial revolution of the late 18th and early 19th centuries. Indeed, it too is based on a mineral and on its transformation by a known technology (that of copper), on an energy resource (wood), and on a development that combines a rationalization of production (on the "hill of the slaves") and exchanges by long-distance transport (by donkey), the whole framed by a strong and stable political power.

The development of distant markets for manufactured goods was, in both cases, essential. Since more could be produced at a lower cost, it was imperative to sell more to justify the investment of the capital needed to develop the new means of production. Obviously, there would have been no industrial revolution if this capital had not been available in England around the year 1800. This is an interesting question, rarely discussed, and yet essential. It necessarily arises whenever the possibility of a new revolution occurs. There is no revolution without capital and capitalists. Who are they, where does this capital come from? These are eminently political questions, in any era. In the last part of this chapter, we will recall some of the events that took place in England in the 17th century around the Crown, a century before the industrial revolution. They can bring us some interesting elements of answer.

The acceleration and multiplication of exchanges are inseparable from an industrial revolution. This is what long-distance trade, and therefore exchanges with foreign countries, allows. The free foreign trade promoted by Ricardo accelerates these exchanges, as we shall see in detail in Chapter 3. It is an indispensable tool in the development of the industrial revolution.

By reducing the cost of production of manufactured goods, and by facilitating their exchange, the industrial revolution makes them accessible to a wider population. An increase in consumption is its central objective.

But eventually, the continuous increase in production finally comes up against the limits of natural resources, in particular available energy resources. Their accelerated exploitation poses two fundamental problems, that of their exhaustion, and that of the damage caused to the environment. According to the work of archaeologists, it is their combination that led to the collapse of copper production in Timna Valley 3,000 years ago.

We are entitled to ask ourselves whether on a global scale this same combination — depletion of natural resources and damage to the environment — will not also lead to the end of the industrial revolution born of coal mining 200 years ago. It is precisely this anxiety that is widely felt today.

But just as the development of coal mines 200 years ago prevented the massive deforestation of England, so the development of new technologies can free us in the future from our dependence on fossil fuels, and thus avoid the climate disruption caused by their excessive use. Some of these technologies are already well developed, such as nuclear energy, photovoltaic panels, and wind turbines, while others, such as nuclear fusion, are not yet available. In any case, their widespread implementation will require huge investments. Where will this capital come from?

The answer to this question is not obvious.

The lack of sufficient capital can explain the very long time lapse that sometimes separates a discovery and its large-scale application, as was the case for copper technology and its derivatives such as bronze. In this case it took 3,000 years between the brilliant observation that the incomplete combustion of wood allows the reduction of copper oxide (by reaction with carbon monoxide) and the industrial manufacture of copper. One of the reasons for this delay may indeed be the lack of capital needed to establish a "factory" on Slave Hill.

5. Science and Capital: The Role of Crown Gold in the Industrial Revolution

By contrast, the speed with which the industrial revolution developed in England is surprising: only a few decades separated Watts's discovery and its industrial application. Watts had taken a decisive step by separating the hot and cold sources in his machine. But his association with the entrepreneur-capitalist Boulton was essential to trigger the revolution. Boulton had the necessary funds for Watts to transform his experimental machine into an industrial one; but he also had a fairly clear idea of its vast field of applications.

The Watts machine did indeed rapidly change all modes of production and affected all segments of society, causing the disappearance of water mills, sailing ships, and draught animals, to name but a few examples; the capital required for this rapid and massive transformation must therefore have been considerable. Where did it come from? How is it that England was already so rich that it could make this investment?

The answer to this question may be linked to a curious chapter in the history of the English monarchy, a history that precedes the industrial revolution by a century.

According to Keynes, the accumulation of capital in England can be traced back to a singular and unlikely event, the 1580 boarding of a Spanish ship loaded with gold and precious stones, the Nostra Senora de Ia Conception, by the Golden Hind. The captain of the Golden Hind, Francis Drake (later Sir Francis Drake), had been commissioned by Queen Elizabeth I to do as much damage to the Spanish as he could. According to the agreement made with Drake, the Queen would receive part of the profit from the booty he planned to bring back if the piracy operation was successful. The contract was executed successfully. Once England's debts were repaid, the Queen was left with a sum of about 40,000 pounds. She invested it in the East India Company, which later became the British East India Company created by a Royal Charter on 31/12/1600 with an initial capital of 68,373 pounds, of which 30,133 pounds were raised by private investors.

Elizabeth was therefore not the only shareholder, but the main one. Thanks to the profits made by the Company, the initial sum invested by Elizabeth I became, after several centuries of continuous reinvestment, a sum that Keynes estimated in 1930 to be of the order of 4 billion pounds. And, no less important, the Company made England the world's leading power. At the same time, the profits repatriated to England certainly helped to provide the capital necessary for industrial development.

The accumulation of capital in England, a necessary condition for the industrial revolution, owed much to an operation of piracy, prolonged by a policy of long-term investment. At the beginning of the 19th century, England was armed to take advantage of the inventions and technical progress that were to sweep through the following centuries. The combination of scientific discoveries, capital pirated and then invested to develop them, and a strong central power is a fascinating example of the creation of an empire ex-nihilo. At the same time, Spain conquered South America and was awash in the gold it stole from there, but did nothing with it. It had the capital, but neither the scientists nor the investment ideas.

6. Scientists and Economists Facing a Double Crisis, Energy and Entropy

The way we obtain most of our energy today is much the same as it was a hundred years ago: we burn coal, oil, and gas. As the world's population grows and people's standard of living improves, we need more and more energy. The risks of depletion were identified and modeled by the Club of Rome in 1970: it expressed the fear of an energy crisis. More recently, it is the emissions of greenhouse gases, mainly CO_2, that have attracted attention because of the climate changes they cause: to call it by its scientific name, it is the entropy crisis — commonly called environmental damage. This is nothing new since it occurred due to over-exploitation of King Solomon's copper mines. Lack of wood was an energy crisis. Irreversible destruction of forests was an entropy crisis.

Over the past century, scientists have made extraordinary discoveries that have revealed new sources of energy. The development of nuclear power raised the great hope that we would once and for all be rid of fossil fuels. Unfortunately, the problem of radioactive waste made nuclear power unpopular. Photovoltaic cells, which convert solar radiation into electrical power, have given us access to an almost unlimited resource. But it is intermittent, and at present we do not know how to store it well on a large scale and for long periods of time.

Moreover, these new energy sources are expensive to develop and perfect. They cannot compete with the cost of oil, which comes out of the ground by itself once a hole has been dug in the right place. On a global scale, replacing fossil fuels with these new energies requires gigantic investments, the amount of which is moreover uncertain. The temptation to carry on as before, hoping that fossil fuel resources are much greater than we say, and that the danger of climate change has been greatly exaggerated, is therefore great.

Since the Second World War, the dominant economic policy has been to accelerate production and consumption as much as possible. In promoting this policy, economists have ignored the risks of a double crisis, that of energy and of entropy. Scientists, for their part, have perhaps not been firm enough in sounding the alarm. It is very difficult to say how much coal, oil, and gas we still have. On the other hand, the increase in the concentration of greenhouse gases in the atmosphere and some of its consequences were perfectly predictable. We will come back to this at length.

Science and capital are indispensable for a transition that we believe is necessary. In other words, this transition requires scientists and economists to work together, not against each other.

Chapter 2

Economists and Scientists Facing the Industrial Revolution

At the start of the industrial revolution, new concepts were developed in very different academic fields. What they had in common was that they addressed the great changes taking place in society as a result of this revolution. In the space of a few years, Thomas Malthus exploited the demographic data at his disposal to draw attention to the dangers of population growth in his book *An Essay on the Principles of Population* (1798); David Ricardo published *On the Principles of Political Economy and Taxation* (1814) in which he presented his thesis on the benefits that free trade could bring to international commerce; and Sadi Carnot laid the foundations of modern thermodynamics in his book *Reflexions sur la puissance motrice du feu* (1824). We propose to begin with a rapid review of these three works. The concepts they present and the problems they raise remain highly topical. We add a few words on the discoveries made by Alexander von Humboldt, a contemporary of our three pioneers who is today considered to be the inventor of the concept of ecology. He was indeed the first one to describe in his book *Voyage to the Equinoxial Regions* (1814) the irreversible harm man can do to the environment in which he lives. The laws of nature are indeed universal and eternal but nature, considered as the environment in which we live, is not.

1. The Pioneers: Malthus, Ricardo, and Carnot

At the dawn of the 19th century, these visionary thinkers formulated the basic concepts essential to the understanding of the problems we face now at the beginning of the 21st century: overpopulation, economic growth, energy, and environmental degradation.

Thomas Malthus, an English demographer, was concerned by the increase in population. Based on the statistics available in his country, he judged that it is exponential, doubling every 25 years. He estimated the world population at 1 billion people. The total cultivable land would become insufficient to feed it in the year 2000 in view of this exponential growth. Malthus's argument was that the increase in arable land could only be arithmetical and that it would therefore be fatally insufficient. In fact, the world population has only doubled every 50 years since then, but the important fact is that its growth has indeed been exponential. Today, we are about 7 billion; we were only 3.5 billion in 1969 during the Apollo mission. If this pace continues, we will be 14 billion people in 2070. Will we be able to feed them? We can doubt it. Malthus was right: exponential population growth is unsustainable in the long run. He therefore considered ways to prevent it, even by coercion. This is indeed what the Chinese communist regime did until a few years ago. In developed countries, population growth seems to be slowing down by itself. But in total, the world population continues to increase in a worrying way. The problem raised by Malthus is still relevant.

At the same time, David Ricardo, an economist, laid the foundations of free trade at the international level. He demonstrated that free trade between different countries, what he called "Foreign trade", leads to a greater variety of products being placed on the market, thus increasing what he called "the sum of enjoyments" for the populations that would benefit from it. Ricardo is considered by many to be the father of free trade.

But free trade does not, according to him, enrich the countries that participate in it. Instead, by drawing on the differences between the abilities and resources of participating countries, it allows people to consume more without working more. This is a remarkable prediction. The feeling of abundance given by the display of a greater variety of products can thus be satisfied. This feeling encourages greater consumption, and in today's language we say that it leads to a faster growth of the economy.

Our third character, Sadi Carnot, is a genius physicist. At the time he published his book, steam engines were at the heart of the industrial revolution, in full development in England. Mechanical engineers were looking for the best way to increase their efficiency in order to make the most of the fuel used (coal). Carnot demonstrated that it has a maximum value which is only a function of the difference between the temperature of the furnace that heated the steam and that of the cold source where it condensed. The larger this difference, the higher the efficiency of the engine. It is a law of nature — no matter how good the engineer is and how perfect the machine is, it is impossible to exceed this efficiency.

If the machine is perfect, the work it does in transferring a certain amount of heat from the furnace to the cold source is sufficient to bring exactly the same amount of heat back up from the cold source to the furnace, by operating it in reverse as a heat pump — but never more, because if this were possible the machine could provide work without consuming fuel. This, Carnot states, is impossible. There is no perpetuum mobile. He was the first to state this principle.

Our fourth character, Alexander von Humboldt, was a tireless traveler. He published detailed accounts of his travels to exotic places, particularly to South America, that made him famous. Today, he is mostly remembered for his observations that cutting trees in the mountainous surroundings of previously fertile valleys had a lasting and possibly irreversible effect on their water supply, and therefore on the livelihood of the people of the land. He concluded that man-made transformations could have a lasting and destructive impact on Nature.

A virtual meeting between Malthus, Ricardo, Carnot, and von Humboldt. What would have happened if our four fellows had met and exchanged ideas? They might have met, as they lived roughly at the same time. All of them cared for humanity, but from different points of view.

Malthus, the pessimist, wanted above all to limit births because he thought that there would not be enough food to go around. He advocated what is known today as degrowth.

Ricardo, the optimist, understood that the industrial revolution was opening up new perspectives. Trade between distant countries was becoming more practical. He demonstrated how it could improve the efficiencies of their combined economies by taking advantage of their differences. To this day, free trade remains the cornerstone of modern economy because it is considered essential for growth.

But is the increase in the "sum of enjoyments" really a good thing? Should we be happy about it? Isn't the increase in consumption that free trade brings about an aggravating factor of the overpopulation feared by Malthus? It is not just the insufficiency of arable land that risks causing famine but free trade can also lead to the exhaustion of all natural resources, including water. This would have been a matter of discussion between Ricardo and Malthus.

There might also have been an interesting discussion between Ricardo and Carnot, who had shown that the work performed by a steam engine exploited the difference between the temperatures of two sources with an efficiency that depended only on their difference.

Ricardo and Carnot might have noted that the free trade mechanism and the thermal machine both take advantage of *differences.* They would have been struck by the fact that they both used *cycles* to describe quantitatively the respective mechanisms through which profit is obtained by free trade and work is done by the heat engine. We shall return in detail to the comparison that can be made between their respective cycles in Chapter 3. This comparison has somehow escaped the attention of modern economists and scientists. It is at the heart of our argument in favor of a renewed and necessary dialogue between these two distinct academic worlds.

The cycles that Ricardo and Carnot described are ideal. But what happens if they are not? For example, in a steam engine, there will be friction between the piston and cylinder. Heat generated by friction will reduce the efficiency; it will be lower than the maximum value that Carnot calculated. It will be impossible to go back. Work supplied by the machine will be insufficient to return to the hot source the quantity of heat transferred to the cold source. The operation of the machine will be *irreversible.*

Similarly, trade may not be completely free because of different kinds of duties, and benefit will be reduced. In our analogy, duties imposed on trade are the analogous to friction in an engine. Both decrease efficiency through irreversible processes. Loss of efficiency means that something has been lost. Carnot and Ricardo may have wondered what exactly is lost, and what are the consequences of this irreversible loss.

It is precisely an example of irreversibility that von Humboldt describes in his travel diaries in the Aragua Valley, several hundred kilometers south of Caracas. There, he discovered that a large lake, Lake Valencia, was drying up. He attributed it to the massive deforestation practiced by the colonists to extend the surface of their cultivable land. Deforestation made the soils incapable of retaining water. Flash floods devastated the countryside. A fertile region became irreversibly unfit for cultivation.

One can imagine what a dialogue between Malthus and von Humboldt might have been like. While Malthus simply feared that cultivable land would become insufficient to support an exponentially growing population, von Humboldt would have told him that the deforestation carried out to expand this land would eventually lead to its reduction. The modern notion of collapse, developed two centuries later by the Club of Rome, can already be found in von Humboldt.

The deep meaning of the loss that occurs through irreversible processes became clear only later. It was not until the end of the 19th century that Clausius and Boltzmann provided the answer to this crucial question. What has been lost is to be found as an increase in disorder, to which Clausius gave the name entropy. The releases of entropy that result from the imperfections of our machines are those that inexorably deteriorate our environment in an irreversible way. If we pursue our analogy, imperfect economic cycles also lead to release of entropy.

Since economy is nothing more than a succession of transformations, its acceleration through free trade will increase this loss and deterioration of our environment.

The work of our four heroes raised the same questions as does our current crisis. Two centuries ago, the environmental damage caused by the imperfections of our machines was in practice negligible. As long as this was the case, that is, until the middle of the 20th century, these questions were only of theoretical interest.

But today, the combination of a demographic expansion that remains rapid at the global level and of a generalized free trade that accelerates the global consumption is an explosive mixture that puts us in danger. A dialogue between the spiritual heirs of Malthus, Ricardo, Carnot, and von Humboldt has become indispensable.

2. Two Communities Splitting

Unfortunately, this possible and necessary dialogue never developed. Economists and what are commonly called scientists, to use the IPCC terminology, belong today to two very distinct communities. This separation is very clear at the academic level. Each community has its faculties and its Nobel Prize winners. Physicists do not have to pass judgment on the validity of the work of economists, who can afford to ignore the physical sciences without running the risk of being criticized by their peers.

There are good reasons for this separation. Physics is not concerned with man, whereas economics is now defined as a social science, i.e. as a science of human behavior.

The separation between physical science and economic science as a social science is not only well founded but also convenient for both communities. Neither has to meddle in the other's affairs. The scientists who produce the IPCC reports will not say anything about the economic and social costs of the measures they advocate, such as the cessation of fossil fuel use, and economists cannot incorporate such a cessation into their models because they are growth-oriented, so they tend to ignore it. While understandable and more comfortable for both communities, it is clear that this separation blocks any evolution that would allow us to get out of the current crisis.

This evolution is necessary. The lack of dialogue between economists and scientists is incomprehensible today. While central bankers continue to inject liquidity into the economy to stimulate growth through consumption at all costs, the IPCC experts show us that the greenhouse gas emissions generated by this same consumption are putting the climate, i.e. our living conditions, at great risk. The central bankers ignore this warning, and the IPCC experts do not care about the impact on the economy of eliminating fossil fuels.

3. The Origins of the Separation

It is interesting to understand how the separation between economists and scientists came about. It may have originated in the evolution of the theory of value. In Ricardo's time, within the framework of the classical economic theory of the 19th century, the value of goods was obtained as the sum of the cost of labor and the cost of the raw materials used in their manufacture. But in a market economy, its value is its exchange value — the price at which goods can be sold. In classical economic theory, there is a link between the value of a good and the physical world. In a market economy, this link is broken. The value of a good is its exchange value. This is why economy has become exclusively a social science, with no link to the physical world. There is no univocal relationship between the cost of production and the selling price.

But in reality, there are necessarily areas where economists and scientists rub shoulders, if not collaborate, for example, in the field of energy. This is because if the concept of energy is clearly defined by physics, it is indeed humans who use it. From the point of view of economists, it is up to them to determine how much energy we will need tomorrow, and it is up to scientists to find the corresponding resources. They will estimate the cost which will be integrated into the economic models.

For example, nuclear power plants were developed in the 1950s and 60s because of the fear of depleting fossil fuel resources. The electricity produced by these plants has indeed proven to be reasonably competitive and safe. But the fear of a shortage of fossil fuels has proven to be unfounded to this day. In retrospect, was the deployment of nuclear power justified?

It is, but for a reason quite different from the original one. According to IPCC scientists, it is urgent to drastically reduce the use of fossil fuels, because of the damage this has done to the climate. We have already burned too much of it. Nuclear energy is one of the ways to reduce their use. This damage was not foreseen 60 years ago.

Nuclear energy was developed for the wrong reasons, and later slowed down (even stopped in many countries), also for the wrong reasons. This strange story illustrates how difficult it can be to make the correct choices in the field of energy.

The true cost of fossil-fuel-based energy is now becoming apparent. It is not related to its production cost or to its exchange value on the markets. As we will show, it is determined by the release of entropy into the environment.

Economists have made a huge mistake by basing their models on the exchange value of fossil fuels. The current state of the planet shows how catastrophic this mistake was. Economists have ignored the total long-term cost of the massive release of CO_2 into the atmosphere, which has nothing to do with the market value of fossil fuels. Economics can no longer be based on a theory of value as an exchange value. It must integrate the cost of what is lost in irreversible transformations.

It must be admitted that scientists, for their part, have not warned economists of the inevitable consequences of the increase in CO_2 in the atmosphere that would result from economic growth based on fossil fuels. Yet, the alarming simulations on global warming presented today by IPCC experts could have been made as early as 50 years ago. One could even say that some scientists have misled economists by focusing entirely on the imminent exhaustion of fossil fuels. This is the thesis of the famous Club of Rome report, which predicted an economic collapse due to this depletion. Evaluation of fossil fuel reserves is a very difficult task. On the other hand, the consequences of CO_2 emissions on global warming were quite predictable.

The current situation is the result of a lack of serious exchange between the two communities. The total separation between economics as a social science and the physical sciences must come to an end. This separation is an illusion.

Physicists claim that their science is an exact science, and as such they can make verifiable predictions. Economists are not bound by the same rigor, because how can one accurately predict human behavior? Economy is not a predictive science. The physicist has to predict to better than a second the moment when his rocket will land on Mars. If he is wrong, we know who is to blame. But if the economist predicts a financial catastrophe and it does not happen, or conversely does not predict it but it does happen, we will not really hold it against him. Yet, scientists should learn economy if they want to have an impact on it.

In the present state of politics, that is, in the management of world affairs, economists rather than scientists, are in power. They have been running the business without showing much interest in what the physical sciences have to say. Most economists have not been trained to understand some of the fundamental concepts that the physical sciences have developed over the last two centuries, such as the concept of entropy. There are good reasons why they should.

4. From Triumphant Liberalism to Alarming IPCC Reports

For economists, the liberal policies implemented on a large scale after the Second World War have given the West a period of unprecedented prosperity. The verdict of history is clear. The liberal policy, based on free competition and free trade, has triumphed over the Soviet model of a planned economy. The collapse of the Soviet regime, followed closely by German reunification, brutally revealed the difference between the levels of prosperity of the West and of the East. Reunified Germany bears the scars to this day.

Western economists have proven that they know how to conduct world affairs in the best interests of all. Of course, the successes of liberal economics are closely related to the progress of science and technology. But these are the same everywhere. The Soviet Union had excellent scientists and engineers who did not yield to their Western colleagues in any way. They proved this brilliantly with Sputnik. Western economists say that it was the liberal policy that made the difference. As Ricardo had already predicted, foreign trade, when implemented on a global scale, accelerated growth and thus brought prosperity to the West.

Growth is at the heart of progress. It allows more and more countries to participate in Western prosperity. The latest and most spectacular proof of this is the extraordinary economic rise of China. Unlike the Soviet Union, it has enthusiastically embraced an essential aspect of liberal economics by joining the World Trade Organization (WTO), without questioning the political power of the Party. Since then, its growth has been superior to that of the Western powers, which has allowed it to increase its

GDP per capita considerably. It can now claim to be a world economic leader. The start of this rapid growth can be precisely dated to China's entry into the WTO. The liberal economy has largely proven itself on a global scale. Economists, not scientists, have triggered the extraordinary phase of prosperity that we have experienced.

However, successive IPCC reports have alerted the governments which sponsor their work to the deteriorating state of the planet. They have drawn attention to the increasing warming and instability of the climate, which they attribute to the high level of CO_2 concentration in the atmosphere. This concentration has increased significantly during our rapid growth phase, from 320 ppm in 1960 to nearly 420 ppm today, whereas on the scale of hundreds of millions of years it had never exceeded 280 ppm. Such a large increase in such a short time has never been observed before. Despite the commitments made by the signatory countries of the COP 21 Conference, the annual rate of increase has not decreased. It remains at about 2.5 ppm and shows no sign of decreasing, whereas it was only 1 ppm 50 years ago. At the current rate, a concentration of more than 600 ppm would be reached by the end of the century, which would lead, according to the IPCC experts, to an increase in temperatures of several degrees and a real climate disruption. Their consensus is that, to avoid this, net emissions should be reduced to zero by 2050.

IPCC experts are scientists, not economists. They have established that there is a causal link between the level of CO_2 and climate deterioration. They did not investigate whether there is a causal link between the increase of the CO_2 level and the unprecedented economic growth that we have experienced.

This link is, however, empirically proven. The increase in CO_2 levels is not a natural phenomenon, it is the product of human activity. This activity is measured by the Gross National Product (GNP). The acceleration of growth on a global scale since 1960 has gone hand in hand with that of CO_2 concentration, as we show in Chapters 7 and 8.

It is therefore not without reason that some people make a link between the deterioration of the state of the planet and the exceptional economic growth that we have experienced for half a century.

Is the limitation of CO_2 emissions recommended by the IPCC experts compatible with a level of growth deemed satisfactory by economists?

This is today the key question. If the answer to this question is positive, there is no need to question the economic foundations of our society. This is the official view defended by ruling circles. But if the answer is negative, the type of economy we have been practicing until now is no longer viable. This opposite view is now gaining ground.

5. Doubt Sets In

The dominant free trade economic model is no longer unanimously accepted. In parallel to the IPCC reports, which are more and more alarming, a popular activism has developed. The hope raised by declarations and agreements made at the COP 21 meeting, which at least implicitly assume that it is possible to replace fossil fuels by carbon-free energies to a very large extent, has given way to a growing impatience in the face of the continuous increase in the level of CO_2 in the atmosphere and the multiple manifestations of climate change that are already present. Considering that it is their future that is at stake, some groups led by young adults, even teenagers, are calling on governments to implement radical measures to stop the use of fossil fuels. Some of the proposed measures may seem unrealistic, such as a drastic reduction in air travel or disposal of all vehicles using internal combustion engines in the short term. But they reflect the anxieties of the young generations which are not to be treated lightly, if we are to believe the IPCC reports.

Scientists, who played only a minor role in the phase of rapid economic expansion, are now back in the limelight. IPCC experts have established by how much and on what timescale CO_2 emissions should be reduced in order to limit the increase in temperatures to an acceptable value, i.e. 1.5 degrees since the beginning of the industrial era.

Can scientists tell us how to achieve this goal? Unfortunately, there is no consensus on this point. IPCC experts do not address this question, it is not their role. It is up to each government to take the necessary measures to limit CO_2 emissions to the level they recommend. No international scientific body has been mandated to make recommendations on the best way to achieve this goal.

This absence is revealing. The scientific community does not seem to be able to provide technical solutions that would maintain the growth so dear to the governments that fund the IPCC's work, while limiting CO_2 emissions as it recommends. We do not know whether, given the current state of science and technology, it is possible to replace "dirty" fossil energy by a combination of "clean" green energy sources that are neutral in terms of their environmental impact, while ensuring growth and energy security at an acceptable cost. Asking scientists to compete with oil or natural gas that comes out of the ground by itself is a very difficult, if not impossible mission. An economy based on massive recycling or "circular economy" has also its limits. As Sadi Carnot demonstrated two centuries ago, there is no such thing as perpetual motion. To recycle products, energy is needed.

6. Should We Sacrifice Our Prosperity to Save the Planet?

We are faced with a fundamental dilemma. On the one hand, economists continue to hold growth as the essential element of our prosperity. This means maintaining free trade. The increase in consumption that it encourages is for them positive. But on the other hand, the IPCC experts tell us that growth based on the massive use of fossil fuels would lead to upheavals whose consequences are in fact unpredictable. There is as of now no proven de-carbonized alternative. Should we restrain growth and our prosperity to ensure the future of the planet?

The origins of this dilemma were essentially understood two centuries ago. Since then, the "Foreign Trade" concept has brought prosperity by extending free trade to the whole world. But it has at the same time accelerated irreversible transformations and thereby disorder in our environment. It is at the origin of climate deterioration.

Long ignored, this deterioration is now our major concern.

Should we finally accept Malthus's point of view and adopt negative growth in order to avoid the worst? To answer this question, we need to understand exactly how growth ensures our prosperity and at the same time damages the environment.

Economics, as a social science, cannot alone answer this question.

The following chapters are an attempt to understand the impact of economic developments in terms of fundamental thermodynamic concepts.

In Chapter 3, we elaborate on the parallel between the concept of free foreign trade of Ricardo and the theory of the steam engine developed by Carnot. We propose a new analysis of the foreign trade mechanism based on a cycle, which we call the "Ricardo Cycle", and develop its analogy with the Carnot cycle. This will allow us to understand that free trade draws on differences between the economies of two countries in the same way as Carnot's thermal machine uses the differences in temperature between hot and cold sources. We will also recall why free trade does not enrich the countries that participate in it. One of the justifications Ricardo gives for free trade is in fact psychological, what he calls "the sum of enjoyments". This concept is surprisingly modern.

In Chapter 4, we return to the implementation of free trade on a global scale and its extension to the free movement of capital. The Maastricht agreements, which gave absolute priority to this extension, are cited and analyzed at length as an example. We stress that free flow of capital is very different from free trade of goods, and recall the objections to generalized free trade expressed by Maurice Allais.

In Chapter 5, we examine the link between generalized free trade, i.e. extended to the free movement of capital and people at the global level, and climate change. We show that the climate disaster announced by the IPCC reports was largely triggered by China's entry into the World Trade Organization. The example of China's rapid development is an illustration on a global scale of the impact of generalized free trade on growth. Ricardo could not have dreamt of a better proof. Unfortunately, the result-ing increase in CO_2 emissions was also predictable. Carnot and Clausius would also have been satisfied with this. At the end of this chapter, we draw attention to the foreseeable consequences of a repetition of the Chinese scenario in India and then in Africa.

It is now understood that the release of CO_2 and other Greenhouse Gases (GHG) into the atmosphere comes at a cost, since they are held responsible for climate change. A hotly debated issue by economists is what should this cost be. In Chapter 6, we show that this question can be answered by using the concept of entropy. The reason why CO_2 molecules released in the atmosphere spread uniformly, whatever the place where they were emitted from, is that this diffusion maximizes entropy, accord-ing to a law due to Boltzmann. Once released, Greenhouse Gases will never get back by themselves to their point of emission. The extraction of CO_2 molecules after they have spread requires an external energy input, which can be calculated. The cost of this extraction is the true economic cost of burning fossil fuel and releasing GHG. Clausius coined the word entropy to make it sound like the word energy, while being distinct from it. As he has shown, the two notions are inseparable. The energy required to reduce the entropy level due to GHG release illustrates this close connection. The International Energy Agency (IEA) is misnamed. It should be called the International Agency for Energy and Entropy (IAEE). This change would put some order in the current debates.

In Chapter 7, we give some examples of irreversible transformations that illustrate the impact of entropy release on the environment. We give a physical meaning to the notion of climate debt, which cannot be erased by financial manipulations unlike the common debt between parties.

Chapter 8 highlights the possibility of a major irreversibility due to massive CO_2 releases: the end of alternate ice ages and inter-glacial periods. This would be a major change in the climate whose consequences are unpredictable.

Chapter 8 highlights the simultaneity, since 1950, of energy consumption and CO_2 emissions increases. We emphasize that 1950 is the year where implementation of free international trade on a global scale started under the GATT agreements, which considerably accelerated growth.

This simultaneity between the development of free trade and the increase in CO_2 emissions, clearly revealed by statistical data, shows that since the fifties growth was achieved without notable innovation, using the same fossil energy resources all along. We insist on the necessity of massive investments in the energy sector as the only way to ensure a sustainable growth by limiting the release of entropy through innovation. Providing and selecting these investments will require a close collaboration between scientists and economists.

In Chapter 9, we advocate a necessary dialogue between economists and scientist that could help develop better free trade practices. We conclude by giving some examples of possible groundbreaking innovations that could profoundly modify the energy sector.

Chapter 3

Economics and Physical Sciences: Ricardo's Free Exchange and the Carnot Cycle

In the previous chapter, we briefly reviewed the history of the separation between economics and physical sciences, and emphasized how this separation has been damaging. In the present chapter, we wish to show that this separation was not necessary.

Indeed, we will show that the free exchange mechanism, as described in Ricardo's Foreign Trade, is based on a cycle that resembles the one used by Carnot to analyze the functioning of the steam engine.

It is fascinating that they simultaneously developed the same concept in completely different fields, physics and economics. Let us recall that Ricardo's work dates from 1818 and Carnot's from 1824.

1. The Historical Context of the Birth of the Free Trade Concept

It is by investing abroad rather than on its territory the sums collected following a piracy operation that the Crown and then the whole of England became rich, through the intermediary of the East India Company. This choice was not obvious, but perfectly justified on the economic level: the return on the investment made by Elizabeth I was more profitable in India than in England. She acted like a modern capitalist whose only goal is to get as rich as possible. Elizabeth practiced ahead of her time a generalized free trade based on the free circulation of the capital at her disposal and at the same time free flow of imported goods provided by the East India Company that she controlled.

Many years later, Ricardo introduced the concept of "Free Trade" in his book *On the Principles of Political Economy and Taxation* published in 1814. He describes a cycle involving the exchange of goods between two countries with different economic potentials: England, a country where industrial revolution has already stated, and Portugal where it has not. Unlike the trade practiced under Elizabeth, Free Trade does not involve British investment in Portugal. There is no flow of capital, just an exchange of certain types of goods.

At about the same time, Carnot presents in his book *Reflexions sur la puissance motrice du feu* (1824) the thermodynamic theory of the steam engine. His theory describes a cycle where there is a heat exchange between a hot source and a cold source. It appears at the time while use of the Watts steam engine is spreading rapidly in England, as we have briefly reviewed in Chapter I. In 1800, hundreds of Watts engines are already in use in a variety of factories and flour mills. In 1825, the Stockton to Darlington railroad is inaugurated. The theory of Carnot is of immediate relevance because it predicts the maximum efficiency that can be expected from the Watts engine. He shows that it is solely dependent on the difference of temperature between the two sources.

The notion of cycle is fundamental in both cases. It allows one to understand how one can take advantage of differences: a difference in temperature between two sources to drive a machine that provides work, and differences between the economic potential of two countries that allow to make a profit.

2. Ricardo's Free Trade Cycle

This is how Ricardo describes the functioning of free trade in the opening lines of the chapter on Foreign Trade in his book:

"If a trader can buy manufactured goods in England for £1,000, have them transported to Portugal, where he sells them and buys with the proceeds a quantity of wine which he had them transported to England, where he resells it for £1,000, he will have made a profit of £200."

It is a cycle where the exchange of goods, of different types, is done successively in both directions. There is no transfer of money from England to Portugal. The exchange rate between their currencies plays no role, neither do wages.

In this description, the profit expected by the trader is the driving force behind the exchange.

Two questions then arise:

First of all, how does the trader know in advance that he is going to make a profit? What is the real origin of this profit?

Second of all, is free trade also beneficial for the common good of the populations of the participating countries?

2.1 *The origin of profit*

In his short description of the exchange cycle, Ricardo does not tell us the origin of the profit that the trader makes. He seems to imply that it is obvious that it exists.

In order to understand why it does, we have to put ourselves in the context of the time. We are at the beginning of the 19th century; the industrial revolution has already started in England, not yet in Portugal. England is a country in the process of industrialization. The value of its products is mostly based on industrial know-how and investment, the cost of labor being only a small part of the total cost; Ricardo makes it clear that the goods in which the trader invested were manufactured products. By contrast, at that time, Portugal is an agricultural country; the value of its most interesting products is based on natural resources (in this case, sunshine) and cheap labor.

It is this difference in the degree of advancement of the two countries that allows the English trader to offer to the Portuguese public fabrics that are new to them, more varied, and cheaper than the locally handmade fabrics. In exchange, he can acquire wines produced locally that are far superior to wines produced in England, which have a low alcohol content due to the poor sunlight conditions. It is the merchant's knowledge of the differences between the local markets and resources in England and Portugal that allows him to anticipate that he will be able to make a profit in this exchange. In the context of Ricardo's time, these differences are very important because the degree of economic developments of the two countries is quite different. We can assume that this is why the trader knows that he will make a good profit.

2.2 *Free trade does not make a country richer*

The justification of free trade does not lie in an increase in the wealth of the countries that practice in it. Ricardo writes it explicitly:

> "No extension of foreign trade will immediately increase the amount of value in a country, although it will very powerfully contribute to increase the mass of commodities, and therefore the sum of enjoyments. As the value of all foreign goods is measured by the quantity of the produce of our land and labor, which is given in exchange for them, we should have no greater value, if by the discovery of new markets, we obtained double the quantity of foreign goods in exchange for a given quantity of ours."

This statement is quite fundamental. The development of foreign trade will not make us richer, contrary to popular belief. But it will give much enjoyment because it will put at our disposal a richer variety and a larger mass of commodities. More enjoyment, but not more value.

2.3 *Free trade and common good*

Since free trade does not enrich the countries that practice it, what is its purpose, besides the profit made by the trader?

The answer is that when free movement of goods is established between these two countries, it becomes possible to manufacture the same quantity of cloth and barrels of wine, and of better quality, in fewer working days.

This can be seen in the following way.

Suppose that the number of hours needed to make a unit of cloth is NcA in England and NcP in Portugal, and that the number of hours needed to make a unit of wine is NwA in England and NwP in Portugal.

If there is no trade, the number of hours of work to make 2 units of cloth, one in England and the other one in Portugal will be (NcA + NcP), and for 2 units of wine, one in England and one in Portugal, (NwA + NwP). If there is free trade and all the cloth is made in England and all the wine in Portugal, the total number of hours will be (2NcA + 2NwP).

The difference D between the number of hours needed to manufacture two units of each, without and with free exchange will be as follows:

$$D = (NcP - NcA) + (NwA - NwP).$$

Free trade is advantageous if it reduces the number of hours of work for the same output, that is, if D is positive. This is obviously the case when it takes less time to make a unit of cloth in England than in Portugal, and less time to make a unit of wine in Portugal than in England. This is called the case of absolute advantage.

But it can also be advantageous if the first term is negative (the number of hours needed to make a unit of cloth in England NoA is greater than the number of hours needed to make a unit of cloth in Portugal Nop) and the second term is positive (the number of hours needed to make a unit of wine in England is greater than the number of hours needed to make a unit of wine in Portugal), namely, if the advantage of making wine and cloth is greater in Portugal. Free trade is worthwhile if the advantage that Portugal has in the manufacture of wine is greater than the advantage that England has in the manufacture of cloth.

Since there is always some relative if not absolute advantage, free trade is of general interest.

This argument in favor of free trade is fundamental. The merchant plays no direct role here. It is quite conceivable that the leaders of the two countries could jointly draw up a list of products for which free trade would bring the greatest advantage, i.e. would reduce the number of days needed to produce a certain quantity of goods.

Two possibilities are open to workers when free trade is established. They can work a smaller number of hours to obtain the same quantity of commodities, or in other words they can work less while keeping the same purchasing power. Alternatively, they can continue to work the same number of hours and obtain more commodities. Today, scientists would say that the first choice is virtuous because it reduces the negative impact on the environment. Economists will I am afraid prefer the second choice because it promotes growth. The free movement of goods is in itself neither good nor bad. It all depends on how we use it.

In any case, free trade benefits both Portugal and England economically because each country makes the best use of its capacities. It is better for both sides if textiles are made in England because it has the means to make them at a better price (i.e. with fewer hours of work) and of a better quality; and it is better if wine is made in Portugal because the climatic circumstances are more favorable there and because the Portuguese have acquired the necessary know-how to make good wine.

Besides increasing satisfaction, free trade of goods is of general benefit. It takes advantage of existing differences between the economies and technologies of participating countries to improve the lot of people.

2.4 *Public satisfaction and increased consumption*

The larger quantity and variety of goods put in circulation under free trade, as well as their lower cost, increases general satisfaction, in Ricardo's words "the sum of enjoyments". The psychology of the consumer is such that when faced with an offer of more varied, better quality, and cheaper products, he will be tempted to buy more. In a free-market system, the people are happier because they can consume more if they want to.

One can only admire the insight of these remarks, made long before the advent of the consumer society. A modern supermarket skillfully uses the sense of wealth that comes from the abundance and variety of goods on offer. We consume much more than in an old-fashioned grocery store, and we are very happy about it. For those who come from an emerging country, the spectacle offered by these supermarkets is dizzying. How can choose among all these varieties of yoghurts, breads, fruits, and vegetables that are sometimes brought from the other side of the planet to be offered to us even when they are not in season? The effect that these displays have on us is a brilliant illustration of the consequences of free trade promoted by Ricardo: the increase in the "sum of enjoyments" is irresistible. The vast majority of consumers will prefer to buy more goods without having to work more, rather than saving money, or working less. Free trade promotes consumption. In the language of economists, free trade promotes growth.

A predictable increase in consumption and an increase in capital profits are two consequences of free trade. In the eyes of economists, to this day, they are both positive, because they promote growth.

But it must be emphasized again that the practice of free trade is justified in Ricardo's eyes only if the benefit from exchange is based on the absolute or relative advantages that derive from the differences between the economies of the participating countries. It is because it exploits this difference that the practice of free exchange allows one to reduce the number of hours necessary to manufacture a certain quantity of products. It is only in this case that free trade rests on a solid basis.

Ricardo describes the reasons why this type of exchange is profitable to everyone:

> "By stimulating industry, by rewarding ingenuity, and by using most efficaciously the peculiar powers bestowed by nature, it (free trade) distributes labor most effectively and most economically: while, by increasing the general mass of productions, it diffuses general benefit, and binds together by one common tie of interest and intercourse, the universal society of nations throughout the civilized world. It is this principle which determines that wine shall be made in France and Portugal, that corn shall be grown in America and Poland, and that hardware and other goods shall be manufactured in England."

Ricardo emphasizes here the dynamic effects of free trade. Not only does it exploit existing differences but it also encourages each party to do even better. British manufacturers will have to innovate even more, French winemakers will have to make better wine, and American and Polish farmers will have to improve the yield of their grain crops.

Free exchange is a factor of progress.

As an aside, we may add that the commercial success is also due to a different appreciation of a given product in both countries. The merchant sells to the Portuguese customers cloths considered exceptional in Portugal but ordinary in England, and to the English customer wine considered exceptional in England but ordinary in Portugal. The trader will make a profit because he knows that the value of the English cloth will be more appreciated in Portugal than in England, and that of the Portuguese wine more appreciated in England than in Portugal. It is easy to imagine other examples of the same type. Oil discovered in an emerging country has little value there; without industry and modern means of transportation, it is of little use. However, it is very valuable when transported to an industrialized country. If the inhabitants of the emerging country do not know this, they will make a bad deal when exchanging their oil for manufactured products. This is how huge fortunes have been made.

3. The Carnot Thermodynamic Cycle

In his famous work on the motive power of fire engines, Carnot's aim was to determine the maximum efficiency that could be expected from the steam engines that were at the heart of the industrial revolution that had begun in England. These machines were used to pump the water that accumulated in deep mines. Their efficiency is decisive because it determines the amount of coal that can be extracted by burning coal in the engine.

Before analyzing Carnot's cycle, it is interesting to note that his theory is based on a cycle that is not the one used in practice. In fact, Carnot does not use the term "steam engine" in the title of his work, but uses the term "fire engine". As we know, the term steam engine is used because hot steam is introduced into a cylinder where it exerts pressure on a piston. This steam is then condensed into liquid water which is consumed. This is why steam locomotives need to be refilled with water periodically. Thus, one of the most prestigious and modern steam locomotives, the 241P17, put into service by the Schneider factories in Le Creusot in 1950, was towing a train of 800 tons at 120 km/h, carrying 12 tons of coal and 34 tons of water, which gave it a range of 250 km. It is in fact the quantity of water to be transported which limited its autonomy.

3.1 *The Carnot cycle*

On the other hand, in the cycle invented by Carnot, the fluid used is not consumed. It is a gas, alternately put in contact with two thermal sources at fixed temperatures, one hot and one cold, respectively, the furnace and the condenser. The gas used has no special qualities. It is contained in a cylinder, and applies pressure to a piston when in contact with the furnace and expands, while it is compressed when in contact with the condenser.

Such fixed-temperature sources do not exist in practice, but to fix the ideas we can imagine that they are very large reservoirs so that their temperatures are not modified by the thermal exchanges in the machine. From the theoretical point of view, the advantage of this model is that it immediately reveals the essential parameter which determines the efficiency of the fire machine, namely, the temperature difference between the furnace and the condenser.

Carnot writes this very clearly in his book:

"The production of motive power is due, in steam engines, not to a real consumption of caloric, but to its transport from a hot body to a cold one."

In other words, it is not really the heat released by combustion that is transformed into mechanical work (motive power) performed by the machine, but the heat transfer.

The Carnot cycle consists of two main phases, a first phase where a quantity of heat Q is transferred from the furnace to the gas, and a second phase where a (smaller) quantity of heat q is transferred from the gas to the condenser. The machine transforms the difference $(Q-q)$ into mechanical work W. Carnot shows that this difference is proportional to the temperature difference between the hot and cold sources:

$$W = (T_H - T_B)f(T)$$

where T_H is the temperature of the furnace, T_B is the temperature of the condenser, and $f(T)$ some function of temperature unknown to Carnot.

The machine can only provide work if it operates between two sources that are at different temperatures, and this work is proportional to the temperature difference.

Inversely, if mechanical work is done on the machine, i.e. if it is working in reverse, it brings heat from the cold source to the hot source — this is the principle of the heat pump. For the interested reader, we describe the Carnot cycle in more detail in the following paragraph.

3.2 *The four phases of the Carnot cycle*

In a first phase, the gas is brought to the temperature T_H by thermal contact with the hot source. The gas applies pressure on the moving piston, the volume occupied by the gas in the cylinder increases, and the pressure decreases. During this phase, a quantity of heat Q is transferred from the hot source to the gas.

In the second phase, thermal contact with the hot source is interrupted. There is no more heat exchange. The piston continues its stroke, the pressure drops, and the gas cools down until it reaches the temperature T_B of the cold source.

In the third phase, the gas is put in thermal contact with the cold source. The gas is re-compressed by the piston under the effect of an external force. This compression brings heat to the gas, but because of its thermal contact with the cold source, it remains at the temperature of the cold source T_B.

During this phase, a quantity of heat q is transferred from the gas to the cold source.

Finally, the contact between the cold source and the gas is interrupted. The piston continues to compress it; the gas temperature increases until it reaches the temperature T_H of the hot source. It is then put back again in thermal contact with the hot source. A new cycle can start.

3.3 *Carnot cycle efficiency*

In total, the hot source has transferred to the gas a quantity of heat Q and the cold source a quantity of heat q. The amount of heat $(Q-q)$, has been effectively transferred from the hot source to the cold one and transformed into work W supplied to the outside. According to the first principle of thermodynamics, which states the equivalence between heat and work (or energy), the efficiency of the machine defined as the ratio between the work done and the heat supplied by the hot source, W/Q, is therefore equal to $(Q-q)/Q$.

There was heat exchange only in the first phase at temperature T_H and in the third phase at temperature T_B. Let us suppose that the ratios Q/T_H and q/T_B (where the temperatures are measured from the absolute zero introduced by Clausius) are equal and of opposite signs. In this case, the yield is equal to $(T_H-T_B)/T_H$; we get back the formula of Carnot, with the function $f(T) = 1/T_H$.

Not knowing about an absolute temperature scale, Carnot could not go further.

We know since Clausius that this function is the inverse of the absolute temperature.

The important point is that the greater the temperature difference, the greater the work done. If the temperatures of the furnace and of the condenser are equal, no work can be done.

3.4 *There is no perpetuum mobile*

The Carnot machine can work in two opposite directions, either by exploiting the difference in temperature between the hot and cold sources to provide work to the outside, or by using work provided by the outside world to bring back heat from the cold source to the hot source.

The machine can alternate between these two modes. But it cannot in the "heat pump" mode bring back to the hot source more heat than was used in the engine mode. This is because it would then have produced energy from nothing, which is impossible.

There can be no "perpetuum mobile".

3.5 *Clausius entropy*

We have assumed above that the ratios Q/T_H and q/T_H are equal. What is the meaning of this assumption?

It is directly related to the quantity that Clausius, in 1862, called entropy. He defined the change in entropy of a system as the ratio of the amount of heat Q that it exchanges at a constant temperature T to this temperature, Q/T.

There is no heat exchange in phases 2 and 4; hence, in these phases, there is no change in entropy. There is heat exchange only in phases 1 and

3, and since it takes place at constant temperature we can use the Clausius definition to calculate the total entropy change during the cycle. The assumption we have made is that the entropy changes in phases 1 and 3 are equal and of opposite signs, so that the total entropy change during a cycle is zero. However, nothing says a priori that the ratio Q/T_H cannot, for example, be superior in absolute value to the ratio q/T_B. The efficiency would then be greater than $(T_H-T_B)/T_H$, and the entropy change negative. But then, by having the machine work backward, one could bring up more heat to the hot source than it gives up when it is working as a fire engine. This is impossible because it would be perpetually supplying work. Decreasing entropy is impossible for the same reason that perpetual motion is impossible.

In short, zero entropy change and maximum efficiency go together. In this case, the work done by the machine can, if stored without loss, be used later to bring back to the hot source all the heat previously transferred, by making the machine run backward. When the total entropy change during a cycle is zero, the machine is reversible. This law is equivalent to Clausius's law according to which the entropy change in a closed system can only be positive or zero, never negative. Clausius was a great admirer of Carnot; it is said that his work was on his night table.

On the other hand, there is nothing to prevent the efficiency of a thermal machine from being lower than the maximum efficiency $(T_H-T_B)/T_H$. The entropy then increases with each cycle. The operation of the machine is irreversible. Operating it as a heat pump, one cannot make all the heat it gave up when it was working upright go back to the hot source. What will be the consequences of this irreversibility? This is the subject of Chapter 4.

4. Generalized Carnot Cycle

Carnot's idea that work can be provided by a machine operating between two sources having different temperatures can be generalized to other kinds of machines operating between two sources with different potentials. In the case of the fire machine, the potential is the absolute temperature. Another example is that of a machine operating between two tanks of water having different degrees of salinity.

For example, a machine operating between the very salty water of the Dead Sea and the less salty water of the Red Sea could provide work. In this case, the potential is the salt concentration, the Dead Sea being the high-potential source and the Red Sea the low-potential one. Such a machine, working in reverse, is called a reverse osmosis machine. It is in fact used to desalinate sea water. It is the equivalent of the heat pump which is a fire machine working in reverse.

4.1 *Sea water desalination*

The operation of a seawater desalination plant is the same as that described in detail in the case of the Carnot machine.

The fluid in this case is water contained in a cylinder with a piston equipped with a membrane that is permeable to water molecules, but impermeable to salt molecules. The piston separates two regions whose salinities may be different, since the membrane is impermeable to salt molecules.

As for the Carnot machine, the cycle includes four phases.

In the first phase, one of the two regions is brought into contact with the source of high salinity and acquires this salinity. A pressure is exerted on the cylinder so that the volume of this salty region increases, with water molecules passing through the membrane but not salt molecules. As long as contact with the high-salt source is maintained, the salt level in this region remains constant.

In a second phase, contact with the high-salinity source is cut off; the piston continues to move, the enclosed water volume continues to increase, and the salt level decreases until it reaches the low salt source.

In a third phase, the enclosed water region is brought into contact with the low-salt source. A reverse force is exerted from the outside on the piston. The salt content remains constant due to the contact with the low-salt source.

When the contact is broken in the fourth phase, the salt content in this increases because its volume decreases, until the salt content returns to the value at the beginning of the first phase. A new cycle can then begin.

As in the Carnot machine, the fluid has been alternately put in "contact" with the high-potential source (here high salinity) and the low-potential source (low salinity). The equivalent of the absolute zero temperature is the zero salinity level here. It is in fact more intuitive.

5. Ricardo's Free Trade Exchange Seen as a Carnot Cycle

We have seen that Ricardo's free trade cycle takes advantage of differences between countries.

By analogy, our understanding of the Carnot cycle allows us to reduce free exchange to its essential elements: a hot source, a cold source, and a mechanism by which the exchange is made. All the rest is part of a machinery which is certainly important but does not touch on the essential.

Here, the difference between hot and cold is that between the levels of development of England and Portugal.

The merchant buys textile from England (the hot source) and unloads it in Portugal (the cold source), where he loads himself up with wine which he delivers back to England. Textile is made in England by an advanced industrial process and wine in Portugal by traditional agriculture.

The transport of textiles from England to Portugal is thus analogous to the transfer of an amount of heat Q from a hot source (England) to a cold source (Portugal), and the transport of wine from Portugal to England to the transfer of a smaller amount of heat q in the opposite direction; see Figures 1 and 2. In the Carnot cycle, the outcome is the work done by the engine; in the Ricardo cycle, it is the profit made by the merchant.

The similarity between the Carnot and the Ricardo cycles is striking. Here, the two countries are two sources having different economic potentials. As a measure of this potential, one could use the GDP per capita. This is obviously a crude measure, but it is useful for outlining the functioning of free trade.

Thus, the greater the difference in GDP per capita between two countries, the greater the profit p made by the merchant and more generally the benefits of the free movement of goods. By analogy with the yield of the

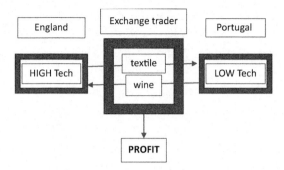

Figure 1. The cycle of Ricardo drawn by analogy with the cycle of Carnot shown in Figure 2. England, as a High-Tech country, plays the role of the hot source exporting textile to the cold source Portugal, from which wine is imported to England. The outcome is the profit made by the merchant, analogous to the work provided by the Carnot engine.

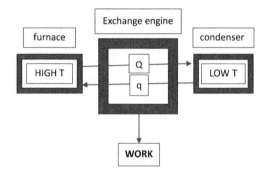

Figure 2. In the Carnot cycle, a quantity of heat Q flows from the furnace to the condenser and a smaller quantity of heat q flows from the condenser to the furnace. The difference $(Q-q)$ is transformed into work.

Carnot cycle, the return on free trade, i.e. the profit compared to the merchant's outlay in Ricardo's example, is given by the following:

$$p = (GDP_H - GDP_B)/GDP_H$$

where GDP_H and GDP_B are, respectively, the GDP per capita of the high- and low-potential country. Free trade between countries at similar stages of development would not be of great interest to a merchant. The example of free grade given by Ricardo, between a more advanced (England) and a less advanced (Portugal) country, illustrates this point. It is because he knows about this difference between the stages of development that the merchant foresees that he is going to make a nice profit in the cycle he initiates.

Using the GDP as a measure of the degree of development of an economy and on that basis predicting between which countries free trade agreements present the most interest can look like a gross oversimplification. But it is in line with the larger number of free trade agreements between North–South (well and less developed countries) compared to North–North (well developed) and South–South (less developed) countries; see Chapter 5, Figure 6.

5.1 *Merchant-initiated exchanges*

In the case we have just analyzed, the exchange is done at the initiative of the merchant, whose only aim is to make a profit. This profit is equivalent to the difference $(Q–q)$ received by the gas at the end of a cycle of Carnot's machine.

But there is an important difference between the two cycles. Carnot's machine transforms the heat difference $(Q–q)$ into work done for the outside world. The trader, on the other hand, pockets the benefit. Carnot's machine is virtuous, in the sense that it provides work that can be used for the common good. The trader is not a priori virtuous. He wants simply to make a profit and keep it to increase his personal capital. Of course, he could also, if he wished, donate it to charitable associations.

But when he invested his money and took the risk of transporting and selling the goods, he did it to make a profit, not to give it away. It is unlikely that he will do so, because that was not his purpose.

5.2 *Free trade agreements*

The intervention of a trader is not, however, necessary to exploit a difference in economic potential. For two countries practicing free trade, this difference opens up the possibility of producing the same quantity of products with less working days. This can be done by the application of a free trade agreement between the two countries, this agreement being an instrument playing here the role of a Carnot engine in the sense that it facilitates the exchange. In this case, the analogy with the Carnot cycle is complete. Indeed, the reduction in the number of working days allowed by the application of the free trade agreement is in fine the equivalent of the work done by the Carnot machine. It is as if the exchange had produced work — the work it spares the workers of both countries. Free trade then works directly for the common good, not for the profit of the merchant.

Besides reducing the number of working days to produce a given quantity of a certain product, free trade can help develop new applications. On the microeconomic level, free trade can be profitable between countries at similar stages of development according to their GDP, in specific areas. It will often be the case that companies in two developed countries have specialized in different fields that can be complementary.

For instance, it turned out in the sixties that some German company had specialized in making high-quality ceramics, which were discovered almost accidentally to be able to withstand very high electric fields. At the same time, a French company was developing very-high-voltage transmission lines. These two companies were brought into contact by a third party aware of the technical challenges and potential developments, helping to build up a very fruitful cooperation and business, highly beneficial to both sides, within the framework of the new European Common Market free trade policy. High-quality ceramics were imported from Germany to France where they were incorporated into high-voltage equipment. Besides the three companies involved, the public at large benefited from this collaboration, whose final result was to reduce the losses in higher-voltage transmission lines, hence a reduction the cost of electricity to the customer and — in today's language — CO_2 emissions.

5.3 *A more quantitative approach*

This analogy between the differences in temperature in the Carnot cycle and the differences in economic potential in the Ricardian cycle is fruitful. Just as the efficiency of the Carnot machine is greater the greater the difference between the temperatures of the hot and cold springs, so the benefit of free trade will be greater the greater the difference in the economic potential of the participating countries.

We have extended Ricardo's qualitative arguments to a quantitative estimate of the benefit of exchange, by proposing to use as a value of a country's economic potential its GDP per capita. This allows one to have an idea of the possible benefit. Thus, Ricardo arbitrarily estimates that the yield of the exchange operation carried out by his merchant is 20%. Why not 2% or 50%? He does not raise this question. His work (1814) actually preceded that of Carnot (1824), and he died in 1823. He was therefore unaware of the Carnot cycle and of his calculation of the maximum yield.

The way economy functions is obviously much more complex than that of Carnot's machine, but we must retain the idea that it is differences that make both cycles productive, and that the knowledge of these differences makes it possible to calculate the maximum yield in one case and to anticipate the profit, or the reduction in the number of days of work in the other. This is the essential point.

In short, Ricardo described in detail a free trade mechanism between two countries, each of which has advantages linked to its own resources and respective know-how. He sees in free trade only advantages, each country contributing the best of itself to the common good. The trader is the genius of the exchange; by identifying which goods deserve to be traded, he contributes to the common good. It is better for the Portuguese to concentrate on making wine than to go to the trouble of making expensive, low-quality cloth; and it is better for the English to make affordable cloth than to make expensive, low-quality wine. All in all, thanks to the transfers made by the merchant, the English and Portuguese will be able to make the same amount of cloth and wine with fewer working days. Moreover, they will be of better quality.

To summarize, the trader exploits the differences in economic potential between the two countries to make a profit.

Everything happens as if the exchange had transformed the difference in economic potentials into work, just as Carnot's machine transforms the difference in temperatures into work. We have proposed that the GDP per capita can be used as a measure of the economic potential of a country. On the macroeconomic level the efficiency of the free exchange cycle can then be estimated by a formula that is equivalent to the efficiency of the Carnot machine. The greater the difference in GDP, the more interesting free trade will be.

6. Imperfect Cycles

The Ricardo cycle we have analyzed is ideal, as is the Carnot cycle. These cycles can be repeated indefinitely. In reality, this is not the case.

6.1 *Effects of losses*

In the Carnot cycle, there is no loss since it assumes that all the heat transferred from the hot source to the cold source is transformed into energy. The maximum efficiency is then reached. But, in practice, there will always be some loss of energy in the machine, such as the friction between the piston and the cylinder. The maximum efficiency will not be reached. In the compound word "free trade", the qualifier "free" means that Ricardo's cycle is also ideal. That is, it neglects all the costs associated with its execution, such as the cost of transporting the goods, the Agios that the trader will have to pay to obtain from a bank the amount of money he needs to buy cloth in England, the taxes and customs duties, and the exceptions and regulations introduced in the agreements. All these factors must obviously be taken into account in calculating the profit which the trader can actually expect from the exchange which he projects to make, or in calculating the number of working days saved. It will in practice be less than this ideal value for the reasons we have given as examples.

In practice, therefore, the exchange will never be completely free. But the freer it is, the greater will be the benefits that can be derived from it.

6.2 *Effects of finitude*

Carnot assumes that the temperatures of the hot and cold sources of his machine are fixed once and for all, that is, they are not affected by repeated transfers of heat from one to the other. But since both sources are in fact of finite size and have a finite heat capacity, the hot source cools down and the cold source heats up as the machine operates. The temperature difference between the two sources decreases progressively, and with it the efficiency of the machine. At each new cycle, it provides a little less work.

We can apply the same reasoning to Ricardo's cycle. The profit that the trader makes will decrease as he transfers more and more cloth from England to Portugal, and wine from Portugal to England, because their markets are of finite size and will eventually become saturated. A more subtle and longer-term evolution will lead the Portuguese to improve their own textile industry, by copying the English weaving machines. Perhaps the English will learn to make better wine. The difference between the economic potentials of the two countries will diminish. Free trade will become less and less profitable for the merchant. In order to be able to continue with his trade, he will have to gradually decrease his profit, until it will become lower than his fixed costs, such as transportation costs and Agios paid to the bank that finances it. At this point, the exchange of cloth and wine will no longer be of interest. The Carnot machine will also stop when the work done is less than the energy lost because of imperfections in the machine such as friction between the piston and the cylinder.

The effect of finitude will be felt more quickly the smaller the size of the reservoirs — the hot and cold sources of Carnot's machine, the size of the countries that practice free trade. The benefits of free trade between two small countries will disappear fairly quickly; they will persist longer between large countries or economic units.

The analogy between Carnot's cycle and Ricardo's cycle is useful because it helps us to understand the true nature of the free trade mechanism. This will allow us to better understand why it became widespread before being called into question recently.

7. The Delocalization Alternative

In Ricardo's cycle, capital does not circulate. Only goods circulate freely, with cloth being made in England and transferred to Portugal, and wine being made in Portugal and transferred to England. Yet, he points out, in some circumstances, it might be advantageous to produce both cloth and wine in Portugal, and to export both products to England.

7.1 *The possible benefits of delocalization*

This would be the case if both cloth making and wine making required more working days in England than in Portugal (a little more for cloth making in England but much less for wine making in Portugal), which is the case of relative advantage The total number of working hours would then be lower if everything was made in Portugal. Since it would cost him less than buying it in England, the trader could improve his profit by making the cloth in Portugal, and selling it as well as the Portuguese wine in England. The cloth imported from Portugal would then be less expensive than that produced in England. Both the capitalist and the English consumer would gain. This is what we call today delocalization.

7.2 *Transfer of capital*

But the trader would have to build a cloth factory in Portugal, which would require a transfer of capital. This operation would run up against the difficulty of transferring the necessary capital from England to Portugal, which was not very convenient at that time. And, furthermore, it would put the trader at risk of being dependent on a foreign government and on its laws, which would be new for him.

In this example, the movement of capital appears desirable only under certain conditions. Ricardo does not plead in its favor; on the contrary he expresses reservations:

"Experience however shews, that the fancied or real insecurity of capital, when not under the immediate control of its owner, together with the natural disinclination which every man has to quit the country of his birth and connexions, and intrust himself with all his habits fixed, to a strange government and new laws, check the emigration of capital. These feelings, which I should be sorry to see weakened, induce most men of property to be satisfied with a low rate of profits in their own country, rather than seek a more advantageous employment for their wealth in foreign nations."

Ricardo had already envisioned that free circulation of capital between different countries could facilitate a delocalization of industry, which could be profitable for the capitalist under certain circumstances.

However, he sought to discourage his wealthy fellow citizens from investing their wealth abroad. He underlined the risks that emigration of their capital would make them run. It is also implied that this emigration would not be in England's interest. Apart from this consideration, Ricardo does not enter into a general discussion of free movement of capital, its advantages, and disadvantages compared to free trade limited to the free movement of goods.

The circumstances evoked — those of a relative advantage — may seem artificial and very particular. They are, however, plausible because there is a difference in the nature of the respective advantages of the two countries. Portugal holds an intangible structural advantage due to its climate, while England holds a more fragile advantage acquired through its industrial development. To make cloth in Portugal, it is enough to invest the necessary sums and to train the personnel to the known techniques. But you cannot make good wine in England. You can transfer technology, but you cannot transfer climatic conditions or any other natural resource.

7.3 *Possible negative effects of a free movement of capital*

The difference in wages between countries that practice free trade plays no role in Ricardo's argument in favor of free trade, since trade takes place without transfer of money. The only thing that matters is the number of working days required to produce a certain quantity of products. Free trade is justified if it makes it possible to lower the number of working days. Ricardo points out that the absence of a free circulation of capital could prevent or complicate certain exchanges that would meet this criterion, but this free circulation is not an end in itself.

Free movement of capital has in fact now become the norm. The difference in wages then becomes essential. It allows the trader-capitalist to enrich himself by manufacturing at a lower cost whatever he wants in low-wage countries. Free trade is no longer beneficial because it is based on an enlightened choice of goods to be exchanged according to the respective advantages of the two countries, an enlightened choice which can be said to justify the profit made by the merchant, and even liberalism itself.

To Ricardo's patriotic reservations about the free movement of capital and people, we can add an objection of a much more fundamental character. If the capitalist decides to relocate production to a country because of its lower wages, there will no longer be any stimulation of industry or reward for ingenuity. The capitalist will become a renter, for there is nothing to say that the number of hours of labor required to produce a certain quantity of goods will be less under a regime of generalized free trade through free circulation of capital than it would be without free trade at all; it may well be higher.

In fact, the two types of free trade are completely different. The beauty of restricted free trade is that it is immediately profitable both to the trader who practices it and to the population as a whole, whom it allows to work less without reducing their purchasing power. In addition, in the long run, it favors innovation. The individual good of the trader and the common good go hand in hand. This is no longer necessarily the case if free trade is extended to the free movement of capital. This extension can be used to exploit a difference in wages (here we should specify to nominal wages, not to real wages), which in no way favors innovation, on the contrary.

This is because the capitalist's only aim is to make his capital grow as much as possible. If it can circulate freely, and if the risks involved can be covered by adequate agreements, nothing will stop the transfer of English industry to Portugal. Not only will this transfer be profitable to the capitalist, but there will also be an immediate reduction in the prices of products offered for consumption. In the short term, this will make free trade, including free movement of capital, very popular. The possible negative effects in the longer term of a free movement of capital were not really relevant at that time since there was no international framework to ensure free capital movement and its associated risks.

The progressive evolution from free trade restricted to the free movement of goods to free trade including free movement of capital, observed since the end of the Second World War, is the subject of the next chapter. This evolution is the result of a series of international agreements that have been progressively put in place. In particular, the agreements passed under the aegis of the World Trade Organization have greatly contributed to it.

The careful reading of Ricardo's texts that we have proposed shows that agreements that include the free circulation of capital are not part of his free trade legacy. The demonstration he gave of the benefits of free trade limited to goods does not apply to free trade extended to the free movement of capital.

It is even possible that in this case, free trade contributes nothing to the common good, and that its consequences are mainly negative. To our knowledge, there is no theory showing that free movement of capital is a factor of progress in the long run. The delocalizations that it allows have consequences of considerable magnitude that have not been sufficiently considered by the institutions that have encouraged it.

Since capital no longer has a nationality, there are no longer any patriotic brakes on the transfer of capital. And as foreseen, the transfer of industries from richer to poorer countries, like between the West and China, has been massive. The question of whether this was a good or a bad thing is today highly controversial. The consequences of this transition from free trade limited to goods and services to free trade extended to the free movement of capital, and the impact of this transition on the climate, are the subject of the following chapters.

Chapter 4

Free Trade with Free Movement of Capital

In the previous chapter, we analyzed the mechanism of free trade limited to goods without transfer of capital. We saw that it exploits differences between the participating countries through a cycle analogous to Carnot's thermodynamic cycle. This analogy has allowed us to better understand the origin of the profit that the merchant makes and why exchange is also favorable to the common good because it allows one to produce as much while working less or to produce as much without working more. This leads to an increase in the quantity of goods put on the market at a lower cost.

We have also concluded that the merchant capitalist is not in fact indispensable. The differences in economic potential that are at the origin of the benefit can also be exploited in the framework of agreements between countries. In this case, the workers will be the main beneficiaries, thanks to the reduction of the working time necessary for the production of the same quantity of products. We must never forget that this reduction is the fundamental result of the free movement of goods. How we can use this reduction — by working less without a reduction in purchasing power or continuing to work as much while consuming more — is another question.

The central question that we wish to explore in this chapter is to understand the consequences of an extension of the free movement of goods to the free movement of capital. This extension may appear to be a natural extension of free trade limited to goods. But is it really of the same nature? We expressed doubts in this respect at the end of the previous chapter.

This question has become essential because of a general tendency towards this expansion, which has been observed in recent decades. Criticism of free trade has simultaneously multiplied. Globalization is being questioned from all sides, much to the dismay of the dominant economic circles which remain fiercely in favor of it. As we have seen, the benefits of free trade have a solid scientific basis. But what about the free movement of capital? Could it be that today's criticisms of free trade are misdirected and that they should really be directed solely at its "free movement of capital" component?

In order to understand the subject, we will start by recalling what the founding agreements of the European Union say about the free movement of capital and what one of their most determined critics, the Nobel Prize-winning economist, Maurice Allais, said about it.

1. The Free Movement of Capital, Fundamental Law of the European Union

Article 63 of the Treaty on the Functioning of the Single Market of the European Union prohibits any restriction on the movement of capital between the members of the Union and between the countries of the Union and countries which are not members, unless it is necessary for legitimate public interest reasons.

The free movement of capital is the most general freedom guaranteed by the Treaty. It is the only freedom that goes beyond the borders of the Union, since it includes the movement of capital between the countries of the Union and the rest of the world. Any European capital can be invested in any country in the world, and any capital from any country outside the Union can be invested in any country in the Union.

For individuals from EU member countries, this freedom includes opening a bank account in any foreign country, buying shares in foreign companies, investing where it is most profitable, and buying real estate in any country.

For European companies, it includes the possibility to invest in companies from non-EU countries, for companies from non-EU countries to take over European companies, and for European companies to raise funds where they are cheapest.

1.1 *Entry into force of the Treaty of Maastricht or Treaty of the European Union*

The freedom of capital transfer became effective with the entry into force of the Maastricht Treaty in 1993.

It should be noted, however, that the Treaty of Rome, by which the European Economic Community was founded in 1957, already clearly stated in its Article 70 (1) that it would work for the free international movement of capital:

"The Community will endeavour to achieve the highest degree of liberalization as regards the movement of capital between its residents and those of third countries."

It is now clear that the free movement of capital, established as a fundamental freedom by the Maastricht Treaty, is the logical outcome of a strategy that has been in place since the creation of the European Community in 1957.

The term "capital movement" has no legal definition in this agreement. But according to the European Union nomenclature (Directive 88/361/EEC), it includes the following:

foreign direct investment,
purchases and investments in real estate shares and other financial products, loans and credits,
financial transactions, such as donations, inheritances, and gifts to foundations.

The Maastricht Treaty goes much farther than the previous European treaties, which originally ensured the free movement of goods and services within the European Community, but not the free movement of persons or capital, neither inside nor outside. But this was its objective from the start.

The extension to the free movement of capital inside the EU is self-evident with the creation of a single currency, the Euro. On the other hand, the extension to the free movement of capital with the rest of the world is a real revolution because this freedom becomes the most fundamental one according to the terms of the treaty. Europeans can invest in the whole world, and the whole world can invest in Europe without limits. Except in extreme cases, there are no exceptions to this freedom. A European, natural or legal person, can invest his money (or the money he will have borrowed anywhere) in any country, regardless of its political regime, even if it is a dictatorship. Vice versa, any resident of any country, democratic or not, can buy anything he or she wants in a member country of the Union. This is guaranteed by the Maastricht Treaty, which binds all the countries of the Union.

1.2   *Europe, a world power?*

The Maastricht Treaty is not a simple extension of the first treaties, such as the ECSC, which established the Coal and Steel Community, or Euratom, whose original intention was to ensure peace in Europe forever by preventing fratricidal struggles for control of basic resources. This new treaty reflects a global worldview based on liberalism in its broadest sense. Its ambition is to make Europe a global power, confident in its ability to compete with the other great powers. This ambition is of a different nature than that of the founding fathers of Europe. To this end, the Treaty introduces new elements aimed at defining a foreign policy and eventually a common defense policy, although what this one will be is not yet clear. The length of Title V of the Treaty, which defines the external action of the Union represents half of the Treaty.

These fundamental changes called for the institution of a European Constitution. This was the object of the Treaty of Rome of 2004, but it did not obtain the unanimous agreement of all the countries of the Union and the project of the Constitution was abandoned. However, the majority of the terms of this constitution were included in the Treaty of

Lisbon of 2009, which bypassed the rejection of the draft European Constitution.

2. Maurice Allais' Criticism of the "Brussels Organization"

Maurice Allais, winner of the Nobel Prize in Economics, was a convinced European. He militated in the fifties for a political Europe, arguing that if Europeans were content with an economic Europe, it would fly apart at the first serious crisis. Allais was a liberal economist and thus in favor of a market economy rather than a Soviet-style planned economy. He explained in his lectures the social motivations that led him to study economics and argued that the origin of the great crisis of the 1930s, which had caused so much misery and tragedy, was to be found in mistakes made in financial management, mainly an unreasonable extension of credit. He tried to build an economic model that would not make the same mistakes again.

Although a liberal economist, Allais became in the 1990s a fierce opponent of what he called the Brussels Organization. He criticized it for having promoted, since the foundation of the Community in 1957, a policy of generalized globalization of trade and capital movements, with countries having wage levels very different from the European ones; according to him, this would increase everywhere inequalities, unemployment, and all sorts of miseries.

He pointed out that these miseries had become much worse in France since 1974, when the Brussels Organization had begun to implement its policy of globalization. He stressed in particular the destruction of industrial jobs in France, at a rate of about 100,000 per year in the years 1974–1993, maintaining that no civilization could exist or survive without relying on an industry. He pointed out that the greater the difference between the minimum wages in developed countries and those in low-wage countries, the more favorable it is for imports from these countries. Given that the population of low-wage countries is in the billions, a policy of free trade with these countries could only lead in the long run to lower wages, and more underemployment, in developed countries.

According to Allais, it is short-sighted to talk about the advantages that the consumer derives from this policy of free trade with low-wage countries, for each consumer is also a producer who lives from his work. The counterpart of the products that he will be able to buy at a lower cost thanks to the free trade agreements will be the loss of his or her job or a drop in salary. The inequalities that will result from this impoverishment will increase insecurity and instability in the suburbs. A limitation of this instability will require social actions which will be the responsibility of the community under the form of additional taxes.

Allais was therefore protesting against the widely accepted proposition, taught in all universities: "The free and spontaneous functioning of markets leads to an optimal allocation of resources." He believed that the blind and unqualified application of this proposition, considered as a well-established theorem, can only lead to disorder and misery.

Allais's criticism of generalized free trade some 30 years ago, and his dark prophecies, were largely ignored. Despite the fame that the Nobel Prize had given him, his point of view remained singular. Perhaps, because of this fame, the dominant economic circles refrained from directly contradicting him. But their silence and the lack of attention paid to him by the specialized media and successive governments were an effective way to marginalize him and indeed to fight him.

However, it is clear that the points raised by Allais are now at the center of a public debate on the merits of free trade. The globalization it has brought about has become the *bête noire* of the younger generation. The economists who run the major institutions such as the Central Banks, the World Trade Organization and the International Monetary Fund are now on the defensive because they are unable to restore confidence in the international financial system, which is subject to uncontrollable instabilities. The governments of Western countries are proving incapable of dealing with the insecurity in the suburbs. As Allais predicted, the total absence of regulation has led to general instability, both financial and social.

2.1 *Where was the mistake?*

Allais' main criticism is the practice of free trade with low-wage countries. This implies a comparison between wages paid in different countries. This comparison is not trivial and deserves a discussion, of which we propose some elements below in the spirit of Ricardo. This criticism is justified, but insufficient. The fundamental weakness of Allais' argument is that he accepts the principle of free trade without telling us the precise reason why its application has led to the present grave situation. This is undoubtedly one of the reasons why his criticism has not been understood. We shall try to fill this gap, and argue that the origin of the shortcomings denounced by Allais lies in the free circulation of capital, now widely practiced, and not in the free circulation of goods. When the free circulation of capital becomes the fundamental rule of international trade, as it was instituted by the Maastricht Treaty, the free exchange of goods and services becomes an accessory and no longer the foundation of international economic relations. This is the point of view that we will try to develop.

3. Was the Maastricht Treaty a Success?

The creation of the European currency, the Euro, and its introduction on January 1, 1999, was the culmination of 40 years of effort. Since the establishment of the European Community, a single currency has been one of the main objectives of the advocates of a united Europe. It is only from this date that the application of all the provisions of the Maastricht Treaty became the rule in practice, in particular Article 63, which prohibits any limitation on the movement of capital both within the Union and between the Union and countries which are not members.

The creation of the Euro was not a goal in itself but rather a tool to facilitate the free movement of capital and goods in order to accelerate growth and its benefits for the Eurozone countries.

Its impact was absolutely spectacular, especially on the balance of external trade payments. Before 1999, all EU member states had a roughly balanced trade in goods and services. From the year 2000, remarkable changes can be observed. The balance of payments of Germany and the Netherlands quickly became a surplus, that of France a deficit, and Italy in an intermediate position.

This differential effect is even more marked if we limit ourselves to the balance of payments for goods. Already before 2000, Germany had a

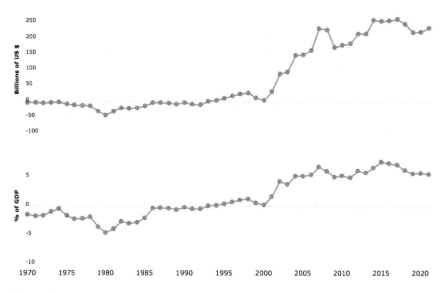

Figure 1.   Balance of payments of Germany from 1970 to 2021. It becomes positive from 2000 onwards immediately after the creation of the Euro.

balance of payments surplus for goods (but a deficit for services). Soon, it became even more competitive and France less competitive.

For Germany, the effect was expected. As can be seen in the graph in Figure 1, its balance of payments was at equilibrium from 1970 until 2000, when it became suddenly positive.

The effect of the Maastricht Treaty on the European economies has indeed been contrasting. It has revealed important differences, perhaps already present before the creation of the Euro, between export-oriented countries and more conservative ones. The treaty has strengthened the former, like Germany and the Netherlands, at the expense of the latter like France. This is shown in Table 1, which concerns the balance of payments for goods only (without services).

3.1 *The particular case of Germany*

The surge in Germany's trade surplus, and also that of the Netherlands, has been the subject of much comment. What Figures 1–3 and Table 1

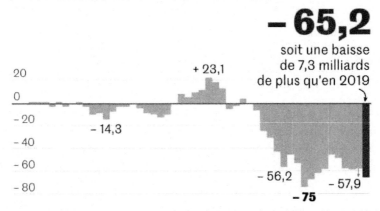

Evolution annuelle de la balance commerciale
de la France depuis 1971, en milliards d'euros

– 65,2

soit une baisse
de 7,3 milliards
de plus qu'en 2019

Figure 2.   France's balance of payments, which was at equilibrium until 1975, showed since a negative balance until the early 1990s. It is to this imbalance that Maurice Allais refers to in his criticism of the free trade policy of the European Community. A much more severe deficit episode began in the 2000s.

Figure 3.   France's balance of payments from 1960 to 2021. At equilibrium until 1990, it becomes positive until 2000 and then falls down continuously.

Table 1.   Evolution of the balance of payments for goods in millions of Euros.

	1980/1990	1990/2000	2000/2010	2010/2020
France	−13	+1	−63	−67
Germany	+71	+59	+213	+218
The Netherlands	+11	+17	+80	+74

show is that this surge was sudden and dates exactly to the introduction of the Euro. This may have been due, at least in part, to the rate at which national currencies were exchanged for the Euro. It may be that for Germany and the Netherlands, this rate was equivalent to a devaluation, leading to greater competitiveness, and vice versa for France.

The year 2000 also marked a turning point in German energy policy. It dropped the nuclear energy program it had been developing with France in the framework of a cooperation for the development of a new technology, the European Power Reactor (EPR). At the same time, it decided to decommission all of its reactors with a final shutdown date of 2022 and started building NordStream 1, through which Russian natural gas would flow directly to Germany.

This was an excellent free trade operation, with Germany importing cheap gas from a neighboring country and exporting its industrial products. Gas is a particularly important source of energy for its heavy metallurgical and petrochemical industries.

The proximity of Russia makes it cheap because it reduces the cost of transportation. The massive switch to Russian natural gas allowed Germany to have a very competitive industry, which became a major source of its trade surplus. Free trade worked for the benefit of both countries.

The cessation of massive imports of this gas, following the conflict between Russia and Ukraine, will therefore negatively impact the competitivity of German industry and could have a lasting effect on the German balance of payments. Its eventual replacement by liquefied gas imported, for example, from the Middle East or the United States, is an ecological nonsense because liquefaction, maritime transport, and then gasification are energy-hungry operations, which ultimately increase CO_2 emissions.

4. Nominal Wages and Real Wages

In Ricardo's free trade cycle, the question of wages does not directly intervene. Indeed, the merchant who is at the center of the exchange does not pay any wages. He does not care what the respective wages are in the two countries between which he organizes the exchange.

On the other hand, if the English merchant decides to produce cloth in Portugal instead of buying it in England, the question of the wages that will be paid in the factory he plans to build becomes paramount. Free movement of capital and comparative wages are closely associated.

A priori it is only if the wages paid to the Portuguese workers are lower than those paid to the English workers that delocalization will be profitable for the capitalist merchant.

But comparing wages paid in different countries is not easy. Let's read again what Ricardo says. One of his favorite theses is that in the long run profits can only be increased by lowering wages. But what wages are we talking about? He defines them as follows:

> "Profits, it cannot be too often repeated, depend on wages; not on nominal, but real wages; not on the number of pounds that may be annually paid to the laborer, but on the number of days' work necessary to obtain those pounds. Wages may therefore be precisely the same in two countries: they may bear too the same proportion to rent, and to the whole produce obtained from the land, although in one of those countries the laborer should receive ten shillings per week, and in the other twelve."

Profits depend on real wages, not on nominal wages, i.e. they depend on the number of workdays required to obtain these nominal wages. It is in the country with the lowest real wages that the entrepreneur will make the greatest profit, even if the nominal wages are higher.

For example, nominal wages are higher in Switzerland than in France, but real wages may be lower. In this case, it is better to invest in Switzerland than in France.

This remark on wages is consistent with the fundamental justification of free trade, which is based on an overall reduction in the number of workdays required to produce a given commodity. In this case, there is a concordance between the merchant's profit and the public good.

However, in the long run, free trade can have a negative impact on wages. If the massive importation of basic necessities, such as grain, makes it possible to put them on the market at a lower price, an entrepreneur may be tempted to lower the wages paid to increase his profits. The worker will continue to work as much, his wage will decrease, but his purchasing power will remain the same. This is an alternative to the optimistic scenario mentioned in the previous chapter, where it is up to the employee to decide whether or not to reduce his working time.

The prospect of a massive development of free trade that would ultimately lead to an increase in profits through a decrease in wages is a frightening one. Yet it is in line with Ricardo's vision of society, whether we agree with it or not. The main engine of the economy is the profit made by investors. But of course, it is necessary to ensure that the working classes, who live on their wages, have the minimum necessary. At the same time, the feeling of abundance that comes from the greater variety of products on the market will increase their level of satisfaction. One could even say that this feeling is a deception, which makes the population accept free trade by giving them the impression that they are getting richer. But this is not the case. Free trade does not enrich the participating countries. It only enriches the investors.

5. Does Free Movement of Capital Affect the Foundations of Ricardo's Free Trade?

But let's ignore for the moment this possible complication.

Free movement of capital puts the merchant back at the center of the game. It opens up new perspectives and makes him an investor capitalist as well as a trader. Ricardo's merchant's interest coincides with the common good. But is this also the case for the investor capitalist?

The investor has the possibility to invest where he likes, he is the only judge. His only criterion is the return he will get on his capital. This criterion has no direct relation with the exchange of goods whose benefit is based on the differences between the participating countries as exploited by the Ricardo cycle. International trade is no longer an intelligent exchange with the benefits it confers.

How will the capitalist choose to invest his money, when the movement of capital is free? It will obviously be, says Allais, in the low-wage countries. But we are talking here about nominal wages, not real wages. For in the short run, only nominal wages count, since they are paid by the investor. The relocation of a factory from a developed country to a less developed country allows for large profits because of the large difference in nominal wages.

It may be that in the original factory the number of workdays required to produce a product is lower than it will be in the relocated factory, i.e. the real wages are lower, and yet the investor decides to relocate because his short-term profit depends on nominal wages and not on real wages. Relocation in this case is not only unfair to the employees of the original factory who lost their jobs because it is based on competition in terms of nominal and not real wages. It is also contrary to the common good because it does not lead to a reduction in the number of working days needed to produce a certain quantity of a certain product.

In the long run, this choice of investing in countries with low nominal wages but high real wages is doomed to fail. The benefit can only be transitory.

The answer to the question whether free movement of capital undermines the foundations of free trade depends on the behavior of the investor. Is he primarily an investor who thinks of the long-term prosperity of the factory in which he invests or primarily a trader who seeks an immediate profit? The free movement of capital gives him both options. In the first case, he will invest in a country where nominal wages are high and real wages are low; in the second case, he will invest in a country where nominal wages are low and real wages are high. In the first case, the factory will develop and produce high-tech goods, in the second case, it will replicate low-tech manufacturing by relocating production to a country with low nominal wages. In the first case, it will be permanent, in the second case ephemeral. In the first case, it will be in line with the original free trade model because the new factories will allow production with fewer working days. It will be done ecologically. In the second case, it will not be ecological because it will not reduce the number of working days.

It may seem counterintuitive to invest in a country with high nominal wages. The immediate temptation is clearly to invest in a country where wages are low. But this second case calls into question the foundations of free trade.

The criticisms of globalization must therefore be qualified. They are justified when it comes to the relocation of known manufacturing processes to countries with low nominal wages, but not when capital is invested in countries with high nominal wages where innovative processes are developed.

6. Short- and Long-Term Effects of Free Movement of Capital

The mechanism described by Ricardo does not require any transfer of capital. In principle, it does not include any investment from one country to another, except in one case, that of a relative advantage and not absolute, which we discussed in the previous chapter. In this example, free movement of capital appears desirable only under particular conditions. Ricardo does not argue in favor of it; on the contrary, he expresses reservations.

Let us consider again the advantages and disadvantages of free trade, and see how they are likely to be affected by its association with the free movement of capital, which we are now considering. Let's call it generalized free exchange.

Free movement of capital systematically associated with free trade agreements of goods opens up a much wider field of exchange. The benefit from free trade remains based on the existence of differences between the countries that practice it, but these differences are now of a very different nature from those considered so far. Some of them may even have disastrous consequences.

6.1 *Short-term advantages of generalized free trade with developing countries*

A large difference between the nominal wages of two countries having very different levels of development can be a major source of profit for an investor when capital can be moved freely in addition to free trade of goods.

It allows the investor to establish a factory in a low-wage country, while free trade allows him to import freely its cheap products.

The combination of free movement of capital and free exchange of goods allows for the rapid introduction of marketable products. It will rapidly increase the sum of enjoyment and consumption, for residents of the country from where production has been delocalized will at first enjoy their increased purchasing power. The consumer will be tempted to buy more. In a regime of free circulation of capital and free exchange of goods, people are happier than in a regime where only goods can move freely because they can consume more. As for the owners of capital (necessary for exchange), they can make more profits. Increased consumption and increased profits for capital are two consequences of this combination. In the eyes of economists, they are both positive because they promote growth. By facilitating delocalization, free movement of capital will greatly and quickly increase consumption and the satisfaction of the public. The trader–investor will make more profit.

Another favorable short-term effect will be low inflation. Consumer prices will stabilize or even decrease by importing cheaper products than those produced locally. With this low inflation, low-interest credit will be available, which will further encourage consumption. This will look like an instant economic miracle.

Developing countries will also benefit from these relocations. The injection of capital from developed countries will result in the creation of new jobs. The wages paid, although very low compared to those paid for the same work in the developed countries, will be attractive compared to local wage levels. The lot of many people will be quickly improved.

6.1.1 *Long-term drawbacks*

(i) Increased unemployment and social inequalities: A destruction of industrial jobs in developed countries will accompany the creation of industrial jobs in the developing countries. The effects of the increase in unemployment on the income of workers will have to be compensated at least in part by the public authorities, which will place a burden on the government budget. To offset this burden, the government will have to raise taxes, go into debt, or both. The effects will be felt in the long run. The combination of increased inequality and increased social costs will create an atmosphere of instability and eventual violence in disadvantaged neighborhoods. All of these long-term negative effects (i.e., longer term than the positive effects) were denounced by Maurice Allais, as noted above. However, he did not distinguish in his analysis between the impacts of free trade limited to the circulation of goods and the impacts of free circulation of capital, a distinction which we believe is fundamental.

(ii) Impact of production conditions on the environment: It may be that differences between developed and developing countries do not concern only wages but also include regulatory conditions of industrial or agricultural production and those governing labor rights. These differences may also be exploited by the trader–investor. They will allow him to increase profit by reducing production costs. In developed countries, the regulatory conditions of production and labor laws are intended to protect the environment and the rights of the workers. They are generally given little importance in developing countries. The lack of protective measures will be felt in the long term. They will include local chemical deterioration of the environment and also increased emissions of air pollutants and greenhouse gases that will have a global impact.

(iii) Impact on innovation: The economic advantage of free trade limited to goods is dynamic and its effects are long term, as it stimulates industry and rewards ingenuity, and makes efficient use of the special resources granted by nature. This dynamic advantage will be absent in the case of offshoring, which only replicates already established production methods. The investor in this case is more of a rentier than an innovative entrepreneur. His benefit is that of a financial operation.

(iv) Impact on the environment through increased consumption: The increase in consumption that it is likely to bring about is in itself harmful. It accelerates the depletion of natural resources and increases pollution, which we will discuss at length in the following chapters.

The added free movement of capital is not a simple addition to free trade of goods. It can call into question several of its advantages. It allows a delocalization of production that can lead to an increase of social inequalities, to a deterioration of the local and global environment as well as to scientific and technical regression. Low wages and poor production conditions offer no advantage to innovation. They do not provide an incentive to do better.

In the long run, the short-term advantages of a free capital movement can be erased by its long-term drawbacks.

Chapter 5

Generalized Free Trade
on a Global Scale

The liberalization of international trade has been extended considerably since the Second World War. In order to avoid returning to the protectionist practices that prevailed after the great economic crisis of the 1930s, and which had considerably worsened this crisis, the GATT (General Agreement on Tariffs and Trade) agreements were signed in 1947. By these agreements, participating countries agreed to reduce or eliminate barriers such as quotas and tariffs that were holding back trade while preserving certain regulations, with the general aim of accelerating growth.

A series of negotiations gradually extended the scope of the GATT agreements, mainly to services such as insurance, tourism, and finance, which constituted a growing part of international trade.

These agreements were eventually incorporated into the more general ones of the World Trade Organization (WTO) that was established in 1995. Strong economic growth remains the main objective of this organization. Originally established by the industrialized countries, it also aimed to incorporate the economies of emerging countries in order to promote their development.

1. Benefits of the GATT Agreements

The implementation of these agreements was successful. Growth of international trade and economic growth of the participating countries increased hand in hand during the following decades.

According to Douglass Irwin,

"The prosperity of the world economy over the past half century owes a great deal to the growth of world trade which, in turn, is partly the result of farsighted officials who created the GATT. They established a set of procedures giving stability to the trade-policy environment and thereby facilitating the rapid growth of world trade. With the long run in view, the original GATT conferees helped put the world economy on a sound foundation and thereby improved the livelihood of hundreds of millions of people around the world."

This quote establishes a causal link between the growth of international trade on the one hand, and economic growth on the other.

International trade had decreased considerably during the crisis of the 1930s, falling by 66%. There is no doubt that trade has increased considerably since the Second World War and there is no doubt that the GATT agreements have favored this increase. The graph in Figure 1 illustrates this increase.

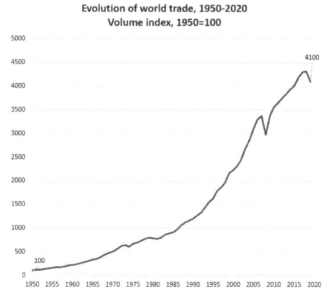

Figure 1. Evolution of the volume of international trade since the end of the Second World War. It has increased rapidly since the signing of the first GATT agreements in 1947 and has accelerated further since the 1990s with the gradual incorporation of free movement of capital, followed by the establishment of the WTO in 1995.

But Douglass Irwin goes further, since he asserts that economic prosperity on the world scale owes much to this increase in international trade. This would ultimately be the justification for the GATT agreements. If economic prosperity is measured by a world production index, this causal link can be established by comparing its evolution with that of international trade. Figure 2 shows the comparative evolution of output (GDP) and trade. The amount of trade is small compared to production until the end of the nineties, then rises quickly. Until 2007, the increase in trade (proportion of trade) preceded that of production, which indeed suggests a causal link.

The evolution of the proportion of trade compared to production is not, however, monotonous. It increased very rapidly in the early 2000s, an increase that went hand in hand with the increase in world production. This acceleration occurred when China was accepted as a member of the WTO — a dramatic confirmation of the impact of WTO agreements on growth. This could not be more clearly illustrated.

The proportion of trade to production reaches parity in 2007, then declines slightly. At the same time, the world production index peaks. Has

Figure 2. Comparative trends in world production (GNP) and international trade (Trade). Until 2007 the increase in trade precedes the increase in production.

free trade reached its limits? Could it be that it no longer contributes much to growth? One has the right to ask this question.

2. GATT Agreements with Free Movement of Capital

In contrast to the WTO framework for the movement of goods and services, there is currently no international framework with rules governing the movement of capital. These rules are usually incorporated into trade agreements (most favored country clause) between countries or between broader regional entities. In practice, many of these agreements allow, with some restrictions, the free movement of capital.

Progressively, liberalization has extended from the free circulation of goods and services to that of capital. International trade has progressively evolved from Ricardo's free trade to a free trade including the free movement of capital, the "generalized free trade". The rules of the European Union, which prohibit any obstacle to the free movement of capital, are an extreme case that we discussed at length in the previous chapter, and we will not return to them here.

2.1 *Reservations about generalized free trade*

None of the long-term drawbacks of free capital movement that we have described in the previous chapter were taken into account by the parties at the origin of the GATT agreements. Rather they were possibly inspired by this early description of delocalization by Ricardo:

> "If the wage bill for the production of manufactured goods, as well as for the production of wine, were lower in Portugal than in England, the capitalists would have an incentive to invest the necessary capital in Portugal rather than in England in order to maximize their profits. The goods produced could be exported from Portugal to England. They would be cheaper than those produced in England and consequently English consumers would benefit from this transfer of production from England to Portugal."

But he hoped that the extent of delocalization would be limited on the one hand by the insecurity of the transfer of capital and on the other hand by the reluctance of any person to leave his country of birth or connections and by the fear of being subjected to the laws of a foreign government. He hoped that these feelings would not weaken and that most property men (capitalists) would be content with less profit in their own country rather than seek a better use of their capital in foreign countries.

One senses in the background of this reservation a patriotic side, as if he feared that this generalization of free trade would ultimately be to the detriment of his country. He therefore drew the attention of the capitalists to the risks that this generalization would entail for them.

2.2 *Extension of free trade agreements including a free movement of capital*

The purpose of free trade agreements which include the free movement of capital is precisely to reduce the risks evoked by Ricardo and thus to allow delocalization in a safe way, if the capitalist considers it favorable to a better use of his capital.

Their number has grown significantly. As Figure 3 shows, their fraction has been steadily increasing.

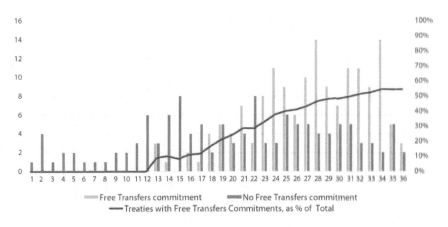

Figure 3. Number of new free trade agreements by year, 1979–2015, with and without a free movement of capital clause. The first agreements with a free movement of capital clause appear in 1992 (year 13). Year 16 (1995) is that of the creation of the WTO.

Source: Deep Trade Agreements Database.

The number of new agreements took off when the World Trade Organization (WTO) was created in 1995. The fraction of these agreements that include free movement of capital is negligible at the beginning, but becomes dominant after 2001, the year of China's entry into the WTO. It can be concluded that the free movement of capital played an important role in the rapid growth of international trade from that year onwards, which then became comparable in volume to GDP; see Figure 2.

The number of agreements increases rapidly afterwards. The year numbered 22 marks the entry of China into the WTO in 2001.

From this year onwards, the number of new agreements with free movement of capital becomes the majority.

2.3 *Effect of the free circulation of capital on the growth of the Chinese economy*

The data shown in Figures 2 and 3 suggest that a massive injection of capital into China took place after its entry into the WTO. Figure 4 shows indeed an increase in its growth in the 1990s, followed by a major acceleration in 2000.

The spectacular increase in China's GDP from the 2000s is accompanied by a growth in industrial production that exceeds 10% per year from 2002 to 2010 as shown in Figure 5.

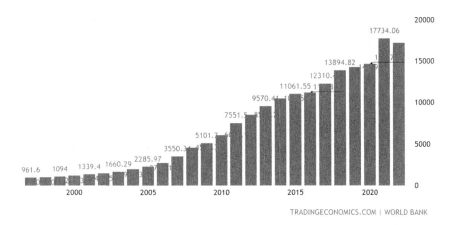

TRADINGECONOMICS.COM | WORLD BANK

Figure 4.   China's GDP shows a dramatic acceleration after its entry into the WTO in 2001.

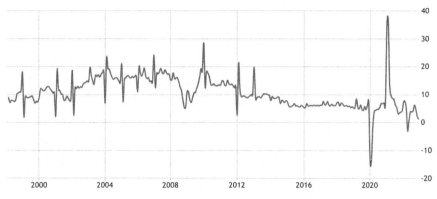

TRADINGECONOMICS.COM | NATIONAL BUREAU OF STATISTICS OF CHINA

Figure 5.   Chinese Industrial production averages more than 10% per year from 2002 to 2010 and then slows down towards 5%.

2.4 *Free movement of capital in North–South free trade agreements*

The massive injection of capital into emerging markets is not limited to China. As Figure 6 shows, the increase in the fraction of agreements with free movement of capital concerns North–South treaties, that is, treaties between developed and emerging countries. China is only one example, obviously emblematic.

It can be concluded that the multiplication of agreements including free movement of capital has played an essential role in accelerating production, and thus global growth, in the 2000s. The economic data thus confirm the validity of the WTO's policy to accelerate growth through free trade. It is precisely after joining this organization that China has seen its growth explode. China's application was supported by the United States, the two countries having signed a first trade agreement in 1979.

3. Impact of Free Movement of Capital on Inflation, Delocalization, and the Balance of Payments

One of the responsibilities of central banks is to ensure that the inflation rate is moderate, around 2%. A moderate inflation rate was indeed

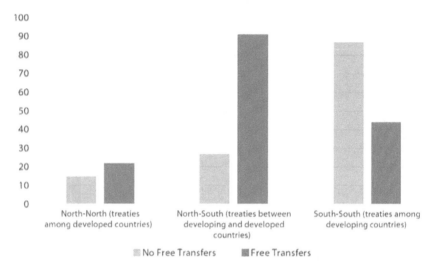

Figure 6. Number of new WTO free trade agreements between North–North countries, between North–South countries, and between South–South countries, with and without free movement of capital. The number of agreements with free movement of capital between North–South countries is the highest.

Source: Deep Trade Agreements Database.

maintained after the Second World War until the end of the 1960s, but then it started to increase rapidly to reach up to 14% in 1980 in the United States, and then went down gradually. Inflation still exceeds 5% in the late 1980s, but from 2000 it averages less than 2% until 2020. These years of low inflation begin with China's entry into the WTO and coincide with its rapid GDP growth.

We see here a clear consequence of the delocalization of industrial production, a delocalization made possible by the free circulation of capital on a global scale. It has allowed the mass marketing of low-cost products. In Ricardo's text quoted above, it is enough to replace Portugal by China, and England by the United States — after China's entry into the WTO and the signing of free trade agreements, including the free circulation of capital, low-cost goods produced in China are put on the market in the US and inflation reduces.

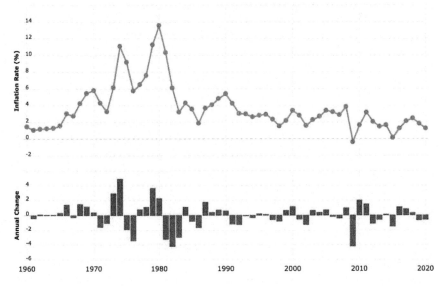

Figure 7.   After peaking at 14%, inflation in the United States gradually declines from 1960 to 2020. For a long period, from 2000 to 2020, it rarely exceeds 2%. This can be seen as the effect of the massive introduction of imported goods from China and other low-wage countries.

Source: U.S. Bureau of Labor Statistics.

3.1 *Direct investment in China*

Delocalization to China has been achieved by building factories financed by capital investment, mainly from the United States. These investments are made possible by free trade agreements that include free movement of capital. Virtually non-existent until 1990, these investments first increase slowly and then rapidly after 2000, when China joins the WTO. Joining the WTO provides an international legal framework for free trade agreements; see Figure 4.

The fraction of these investments in relation to GDP increases rapidly at first, then decreases gradually as GDP increases considerably.

3.2 *Impact of delocalization on the balance of payments between the US and China*

At the same time, delocalization leads to a deficit in the trade balance. Much of what used to be manufactured in the United States is now

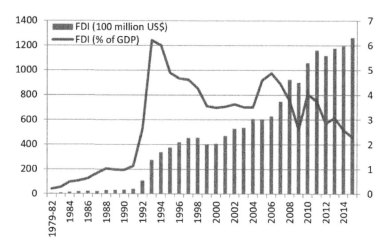

Figure 8. Foreign Direct Investment (FDI) in China, takes off in 1991, reaches a plateau until year 2000, then increases rapidly after China's entry into the WTO. As a percentage of GDP, FDI has decreased. While it played a decisive role in jump starting China's economy, it is now relatively less important.

Source: World Bank.

produced in China. Until the end of the nineties, there is little import from China. As soon as the first trade agreements are signed, imports grow and become massive after China joins the WTO, leading to a large deficit as can be seen Figure 9.

We have focused here on the impact of trade agreements on the deficit of the US in its exchanges with China. Trade agreements with other Asian countries have had a similar impact. The same applies also to many other western countries, such as between France and China. The deficit in the balance of payments of France with China has increased from about 5 billion to 40 billion Euros since 2000.

In the EU, Germany is the exception. As can be seen from Figures 10 and 11 trade has indeed surged after China joined the WTO, but exports and imports are roughly in balance, at a level of about 100 billion Euros.

4. Stagnation of Exchanges Since 2010

After the great financial crisis of 2008, the number of new agreements saturated and then declined; see Figure 12.

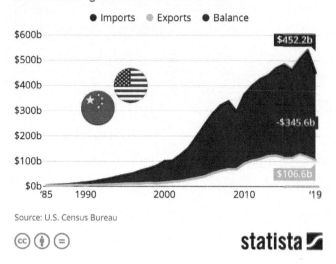

Figure 9. The US trade deficit with China becomes massive after its entry into the WTO in 2000.

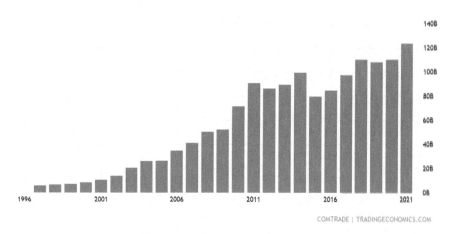

Figure 10. Exports from Germany to China have surged after China joined the WTO in 2000.

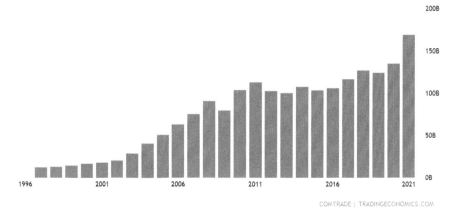

Figure 11. Imports from China to Germany have surged at the same time as exports. Contrary to the case of the US, trade has remained roughly balanced since then.

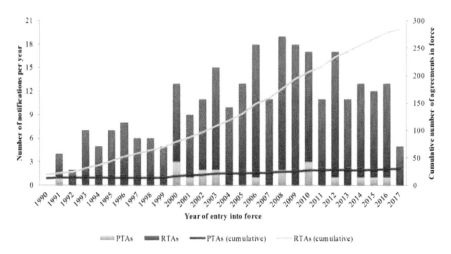

Figure 12. The number of new free trade agreements (blue) peaks in 2008 and then declines significantly.

This saturation, then this decrease, marks a turning point since in the post-war years the multiplication of free trade agreements was considered as the central objective of a globalization economy preached by the World Trade Organization. Is this a passing effect of the 2008 financial crisis or is it a sign of the harbinger of a deeper change in international trade?

This last interpretation is supported by the global evolution of international trade; see Figure 13. It shows a first stage of growth from the mid-1970s, followed by a second one from the 2000s onwards. This phase ends around 2010. Since then, international trade saturated, as did the number of new free trade agreements.

This evolution of international trade shows how much it depends on the continuous implementation of new free trade agreements.

The first stage of growth corresponds to the implementation of the GATT agreements, first of all between Western economies. The second one corresponds to the entry of China and many other Asian countries into the WTO.

Only Africa remains to be integrated. For the time being, this integration is still pending.

The recent saturation of international trade coincides with a profound change in direct investment under free trade agreements that include free capital flows, for example, between the United States and China. As Figure 14 shows, until 2009, the United States invests in China but China

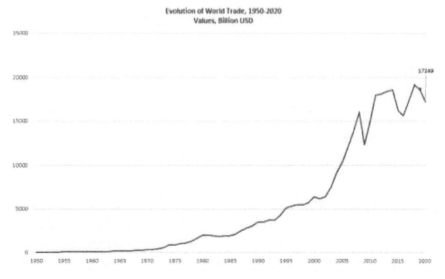

Figure 13. Evolution of international trade since 1950. Negligible until the early 1970s, it grew with the entry into force of the GATT agreements, and then after China's entry into the World Trade Organization in 2000. It has stagnated since 2010.

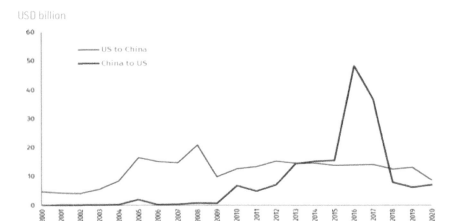

Source: Rhodium Group.

Figure 14.   US direct investment in China (blue) and China in the United States (red). They were very unbalanced until 2009, but have since become more balanced.

does not invest in the United States. The direction of investment then reverses, to stabilize at about equilibrium recently.

This evolution illustrates a remarkable fact: in the space of 20 years, China's economy has gone from being an emerging economy to a mature economy. It has become rich enough to be able to invest abroad, whereas up to 20 years ago its development took place thanks to foreign investments.

4.1 *Exhaustion of the effects of free trade on the development of international trade*

As Figure 9 shows, the phase of rapid trade development up to 2010 corresponds to the period of one-way direct investment from the United States to China. We see here an exemplary illustration of the mechanism that makes free trade attractive, a mechanism discussed at length in the previous chapter. As Ricardo suggested, and as we have analyzed in detail, it is precisely when the differences between the potentials of two economies are greatest that free trade is most profitable, that is, when it generates the greatest profits. These profits persist as long as the differences remain large. Eventually, they will necessarily diminish, profits will fall and with them the level of trade.

The free movement of capital, which was not part of the original free trade, has played the role of an accelerator here. It allowed a massive delocalization of industrial production, made profitable by the great difference between nominal wages. China then rapidly became richer, until it became the industrial equal of the United States. Differences then narrowed, and trade slowed down. The current saturation is probably a transitory phenomenon, which will be followed by a decrease in trade.

4.2 *Questioning the benefits of free trade*

The saturation of international trade seems to have turned the traditional proponents of free trade on their head. It was supposed to ensure prosperity forever, but this promise does not seem to be kept. Economic growth is declining, while the social inequalities accentuated by globalization are increasing. The massive deindustrialization of some Western countries has aggravated the social tensions already denounced by Maurice Allais some 30 years ago. Free trade is more and more criticized. From being a universal panacea for ensuring prosperity through growth for all and forever, it is now seen by some as the culprit for all ills, from increasing social inequality to environmental degradation and climate change.

This questioning is not the expression only of political protest movements, or even anarchists. It has spread to the leading political circles.

In this regard, it is worth noting the change in Germany's free trade policy. As the most powerful country in the European Union, it had played a major role in formulating and implementing a complete opening of the free movement of capital, in particular by making it the cornerstone of the European economy. Remember, this total openness means that any European asset can be acquired by any non-European agent, from any country. It is a fundamental law of the EU that no member country can on its own oppose such an acquisition.

The only exception is in matters of defense involving public security. This is what Germany did recently (2020) by blocking the acquisition of a company (IMST) specializing in satellite communications.

Furthermore, Brussels has qualified China as both a partner and a systemic competitor, and is preparing defensive measures to prevent certain acquisitions.

From its side, Washington has taken measures to prevent Chinese companies from setting up shop in the United States and has limited their access to Wall Street. It has also increased tariffs for certain products such as solar panels.

This is a market largely dominated by China, while the basic technology (silicon cells) was developed in the United States.

Massive investments in the USA and Europe are underway to limit their dependencies in certain critical areas such as semiconductors and the pharmaceutical industry. Free trade is now largely in question. The period of easy gains is over; other considerations come into play.

4.3 *Whose fault is it?*

In our opinion, the current setbacks do not call into question the free trade itself, which rests on a solid scientific foundation, as we have shown in the previous chapter.

But it calls into question its extension to the free movement of capital, which was done outside of any rules. This extension allowed investors to earn a lot of money very fast, exploiting large differences in nominal wages, without investing in innovation to produce more and better with less work.

In this practice, free trade of goods plays only a secondary role. It is the free movement of capital that is the essential ingredient that allows the investor to make a profit.

Free movement of capital has accelerated economic and social transformations that would have taken place anyway, but much more slowly if free trade had been limited to the exchange of goods. It is the rapid pace of transformations which is at the origin of the social distortions denounced by Maurice Allais before anyone else did.

It also erased differences, standardizing in two decades economies that were originally very different, resulting in a decrease in global growth.

This does not mean that free movement of capital is a bad thing in itself. It all depends on how it is being used.

Chapter 6

Irreversibility and Entropy Release: The Climate Debt

The ideal Carnot and Ricardo cycles are virtuous because they are reversible. An ideal Carnot machine can turn backwards and make all the heat that has been transferred to the cold source flow back to the hot source. It works without increasing entropy. Similarly, in an ideal Ricardian cycle, transfers of cloth and wine between England and Portugal are reversible: the trader can use the profit he has made to send the wine back to Portugal, exchange it at a loss for the English cloth he has brought, and send the latter back to England. The absence of irreversibility means that entropy does not increase.

But in practice, there are no ideal cycles. Irreversibility cannot be completely avoided. According to Carnot and Clausius, there will be an increase in entropy, which will be released to the environment. These releases include air and water pollution, and an increase in the CO_2 content of the atmosphere.

Since their consequences can be dramatic, the limitation of entropy releases has become a priority. The progress does not consist anymore in increasing our energy resources in order to be able to increase our consumption, but in decreasing the entropic releases of the existing resources or at least to privilege those which do not release any or very little. The fear is no longer to run out of energy but to succumb to the consequences of entropy releases, releases due to the irreversible processes that accompany the production and use of energy. It is a paradigm shift.

1. Some Concrete Examples of Irreversibility

1.1 *Combustion*

Free combustion of any fuel is irreversible for two distinct reasons. First, because the heat released by the chemical reaction, in which one carbon atom and two oxygen atoms combine to form a molecule of CO_2, is transferred to the surrounding air where it diffuses. This heat thus becomes unrecoverable. But then, the CO_2 molecules spread in the atmosphere and this phenomenon is also irreversible. No matter where they were emitted from, they can be found anywhere in the atmosphere after a few months. Their diffusion on a planetary scale is a remarkable effect. The molecules emitted, for example, in China do not remain concentrated there. They can be found after some time at the South Pole as well as anywhere in the atmosphere. This diffusion is proved by measurements of the CO_2 concentration in different places on the planet, which show that it is the same everywhere, for example, in the South Pole, where no fuel is burned, and in industrialized areas like China where a lot of fuel is burned.

For these two distinct reasons — the loss of heat and the diffusion of CO_2 molecules — burning is irreversible. The loss of heat is a loss of energy that reduces our reserves. This is what has attracted attention so far. But in the long run, the diffusion of CO_2 molecules can be more dangerous; this is the problem of climate change.

In general, irreversibility implies, as we have seen in the case of the Carnot fire machine, that running backwards requires an energy input. This applies as well to the irreversibility of the diffusion of CO_2 molecules in the atmosphere!

In a later section of this chapter, we will come back to the history of CO_2 emissions and the reasons why their impact on the climate is feared. We will see how, with the help of Boltzmann's theory, it is possible to calculate the minimum energy cost that would be required to extract them back.

1.2 *Imperfect Carnot machine*

In the case of free air combustion, to use Carnot's language, the caloric has been expended but no work has been done. But in the case of a Carnot machine, which exploits the temperature difference between hot and cold sources and not the caloric itself, some work is done. However, since the machine is imperfect, its operation is not reversible.

Let's consider the case of a thermal machine where the movement of the piston is done with friction, which is always the case in practice. This friction produces a certain heat QF per cycle. This heat, lost, must be deducted from the work done — the efficiency of the machine is no longer the maximum efficiency. At the same time, the entropy change during a cycle is no longer zero. The entropy increases by a term QF/T. The entropy changes in the phases 1 and 3 of the cycle do not compensate each other anymore. The decrease of energy efficiency and the increase of entropy go hand in hand.

Frictional heating is an irreversible transformation at the microscopic scale. Small metal particles are torn away from the surfaces of the piston and of the cylinder in which it moves. Part of the work done by the machine is spent in this removal; the efficiency decreases.

A second effect, which is also irreversible, is that the particles produced are dispersed in the engine oil, which has the specific function of reducing friction. The efficiency of the oil decreases, the output decreases even more.

Eventually, these particles will have to be removed, because they not only reduce the efficiency of the engine but also cause damage to the machine. The oil polluted by particles is thrown away and replaced by new oil.

In this example, the diffusion of particles in the oil illustrates the increase in entropy. Draining is the method used to eliminate this excess entropy, or more precisely to discharge it to the outside. Eventually, the used oil will have to be treated or burned.

As in any irreversible transformation, entropy is released. The reversal consists in replacing the polluted oil by clean oil. This replacement, as well as the treatment of the used oil, has a cost that can be calculated. This is the short-term effect of elimination of the rejected entropy. As for the basic irreversible phenomenon, the tearing off of particles from the surfaces of the piston and cylinder, it will require in the long run engine reconditioning.

This example illustrates how a microscopic irreversible phenomenon — here the tearing off of micro-particles — results in a decrease in efficiency, an excess of entropy (diffusion of these particles in the engine oil), and at the end a release of this entropy towards the environment.

The above remarks always apply, but to a degree that depends on the efficiency of the machine. The closer it gets to the maximum Carnot efficiency, the less energy it will take to go backwards.

The conclusions that one can draw from the above examples of irreversibility — combustion and friction — are of a general character. Any irreversibility is accompanied by a decrease in efficiency and an entropy increase, eventually released to the environment. In the long run, this increase in entropy can have more harmful consequences than the loss of efficiency itself, as in the case where the engine is put out of action. This is the case for all pollution-type phenomena. It may be necessary to turn back the clock, which may require a very large investment in energy.

1.3   *Sea water desalination*

The lack of drinking water is today a major problem that affects a growing fraction of the world's population. In many regions, desalination of sea water has become a necessity to ensure the survival of populations.

Desalinating seawater is similar to extracting CO_2 molecules from the atmosphere, as we will discuss below. To desalinate water, it is necessary to decrease its entropy level. Hence, energy is needed.

Desalination is today an industrial process whose energy cost is known. This cost can be used as a basis to estimate the cost of CO_2 extraction from the atmosphere, if this extraction should become necessary.

According to published data, it takes about 3 kWh of energy to desalinate 1 m^3 of sea water. In a semi-arid country like Israel, a significant fraction of the water used is obtained by desalination. The total water consumption is about 120 l per person per day. If all the water used in Israel were obtained in this way, the power required would represent more than 5% of all electricity production, equivalent to what would provide a medium-sized nuclear power plant (500 MW).

California's climate is similar to Israel's, and its water resources are also limited. It gets much of its water from the Colorado River. If that source were to dry up, California would need to build nuclear power plants with a total capacity of about 10 GW to produce the necessary water, because its population is 4 times higher than that of Israel and the water consumption per capita is about 5 times higher.

Approximately 100 million cubic meters of desalinated water is produced per day worldwide. The power used is about 200 GW, which is about half of the world's nuclear power. It is expected that climate change coupled with population growth in emerging countries will lead to an increasing demand for clean water. The needed power will increase accordingly. For developing countries, this will require a substantial fraction of the overall energy consumption.

2. Global Irreversibility: Greenhouse Gases

Irreversibility is nowadays at the center of the climate problem. This is because the increase of CO_2 concentration in the atmosphere is the result of the combustion of coal, gas, and oil, of different loss mechanisms in a variety of transformations, and of the diffusion of CO_2 molecules, which are all irreversible.

In the case of engine oil pollution resulting from friction between piston and cylinder, it is necessary to change the oil. If it is not done, the engine is condemned in the short term. In the case of CO_2 emissions into the atmosphere due to the combustion of fossil fuels, the same basic elements are present: irreversibility and entropy release. But when and how can one drain, and what will be the cost?

These questions sum up the climate challenge in a few words. As we can see, they mix the purely scientific aspect — when to drain and how to do it — and the economic aspect — how much will it cost.

The first question is probably the most difficult one to answer. Is there a concentration of CO_2 above which the climate becomes unstable? Have we already exceeded it, or are we still within this concentration? In the first case, CO_2 extraction is an urgent matter. In the second case, it can wait. In the case of seawater, we know how much saltiness is tolerable. But by how much can we let the CO_2 concentration increase?

Climate scientists alone cannot answer this question. But we can estimate the cost of extracting CO_2 molecules in excess. We will show that it is considerable.

2.1 *Application of Boltzmann's law to seawater desalination and to the extraction of excess CO_2 from the atmosphere*

Boltzmann's law says that the entropy increase caused by the introduction of a foreign molecule in the atmosphere is equal to the product of a universal constant, the Boltzmann constant k_B, by the Neperian logarithm of the number of countable configurations that this molecule can explore. This increase in entropy, multiplied by the absolute temperature (i.e. expressed in degrees Kelvin which are counted from absolute zero) of the atmosphere, gives the minimum energy that would have to be invested to extract this molecule.

For small concentrations, the entropy change is equal to the number of molecules introduced multiplied by the Boltzmann constant and by the logarithm of the concentration. This entropy change, multiplied by the temperature, gives the energy that must be supplied to extract these molecules.

To begin with, and as a comparison, we can apply Boltzmann's law to the calculation of the energy needed for the desalination of sea water. Indeed, the two problems — extraction of salt molecules from seawater and extraction of CO_2 molecules from the atmosphere — are of the same nature.

The salt concentration of sea water is about 35,000 ppm. The number of molecules of salt per cubic meter of sea water is about 1×10^{27}. Applying Boltzmann's law, we find that the energy required to extract them is about 4 kWh. For several reasons, this result is only approximate, in particular because Boltzmann's law only applies to large dilutions. What is important to remember is that we find that the calculation based on Boltzmann's law gives energy of the same order as the one quoted as an empirical result by the industry, i.e. from 3 to 5 kWh.

We can therefore confidently use the same method to calculate the energy needed to extract CO_2 from the atmosphere. The current concentration of CO_2 is about 400 ppm and the excess of CO_2 is about 100 ppm. This excess amounts to 1.1040 molecules. A return to equilibrium requires its extraction. We find that the necessary energy, given by Boltzmann's law as stated above, is 33×10^{19} Joule, or 1×10^{14} kWh.

A power of 10,000 GW, i.e. the power supplied by 10,000 nuclear power plants, each providing a power of 1 GW, would be necessary to eliminate in 1 year all the excess of CO_2. If we only want to eliminate the excess of CO_2 in 10 years, we would have to devote the energy supplied by 1,000 nuclear power plants. To put it in perspective, there are less than 500 of them in the world today. They could just about eliminate the excess of CO_2 in 20 years. It is interesting to note that the power needed to extract 1 ppm of CO_2 from the atmosphere each year, i.e. 100 GW, is of the same order as that consumed today in the world to desalinate sea water.

3. The Climate Debt

Our estimate of the energy cost of CO_2 capture in order to return to its pre-industrial concentration level is only an order of magnitude. Indeed, our calculation does not take into account the different losses due to technical imperfections, as it is the case for the calculation of the thermodynamic Carnot efficiency. It is only a lower bound. But this calculation has the merit to allow us to quantify the notion of climate debt.

This debt is huge. If it had to be repaid in a few years under penalty of an ecological catastrophe, it would be necessary to devote to it the totality of the production of non-carbon energy by the nuclear power stations, photo-voltaic systems, the windmills, and others. It would also be necessary to stop all CO_2 emissions.

Translated into budget terms, based on a kWh price of US$ 0.2, our calculation gives a minimum extraction cost of about US$ 30/ton of CO_2. The energy production that would be needed to capture all the CO_2 in excess would cost a sum of 20,000 billion dollars. This amount is in the order of the annual GDP of the United States. As CO_2 emissions continue, the concentration increases by 2 to 3 ppm per year. The debt thus increases by 400 to 600 billion dollars per year.

By way of comparison, the major investment plan recently passed by the U.S. Congress, considered extremely ambitious and at the limit of what the U.S. economy can support, would cost less than US$1,000 billion per year.

In recent years, several groups have begun to develop methods of direct capture of CO_2 from the atmosphere (DAC, Direct Air Capture).

The most advanced one, installed in Ireland, captures 4,000 tons of CO_2 per year which is stored in natural underground reservoirs. The extraction costs quoted are in the order of 500 US*/ton of CO_2. They are higher than the lower bound of 30 US$/ton that we have calculated, which is quite credible. The proponents are aiming for a cost of 100 US$/ton, which is also credible. But it is so high that extracting all the excess atmospheric CO_2 seems out of reach.

3.1 *How did we get there?*

Carnot could not have made our calculation because Boltzmann's law of entropy was not yet known. He could only be concerned with the efficiency of his machine, that is, with the best possible use of the fuel. He could not worry about the effects of the release of entropy on the environment, because this notion did not exist yet. These effects are now our major concern.

Likewise, Ricardo could not have been concerned with the increase in consumption that would result from the free trade he was advocating. He could not have known that, because all consumption requires irreversible transformations, this increase would eventually result in damage to the environment because of more entropy release to the environment.

But more than a century has passed since we have the scientific evidence to understand the link between consumption and entropy release, and its consequences. Since the 1960s, when fossil fuel consumption went into overdrive, one could have predicted that the increase in atmospheric CO_2 would become a major problem 50 years later. The increase from 320 ppm to 420 ppm has changed the climate outlook. By going from 20 ppm to 120 ppm, the excess CO_2 has become a heavy climate debt. We risk paying dearly for these years of reckless growth. The climate debt is obviously owed by the polluting countries, in proportion to their accumulated emissions. They are known.

To use the language of economists, the question is whether this debt is sustainable or not. CO_2 emissions are debt emissions. The creditor is Mother Nature. As long as she is willing to give credit, everything is fine, and we can continue to be in debt. But she has not informed us about our credit line. Have we already exceeded it, are we going to exceed it soon, or is the limit so high that we do not need to worry about it? This crucial question is discussed in detail in the next chapter.

4. Influence of Free Trade on Climate Debt

Is there a relationship between climate debt, scientifically defined above, and free trade? The answer to this question depends on whether one considers free trade limited to the free movement of goods, or free trade extended to the free movement of capital.

4.1 *Free trade limited to the movement of goods*

When trade is not free — for example, if there are tariffs — the benefits that parties can draw from the trade is reduced. They have fewer reasons to specialize in what they do best. To return to Ricardo's example, England will have fewer reasons to specialize in cloth making and Portugal in wine production. The overall economy of the two participating countries will be less efficient. In total, there will be more entropy release, since it will take more labor hours, thus energy, to get the same output. This increase in entropy release will manifest itself, for example, in more CO_2 emissions for the same production. Ricardo's approach is similar to Carnot's; he is looking for the optimum yield. The liberalization of trade between countries allows the production of the same quantity of goods with less labor and less use of natural resources than if each country did everything by itself. The economic efficiency of two countries practicing free trade will be greater than if they operated separately.

All production requires irreversible transformations, which ultimately result in the release of entropy; this cannot be avoided. But since in Ricardo's cycle the production of the same product is achieved with less work (i.e. it uses less energy and fewer natural resources), it causes less entropy to be released.

As a result, Ricardo's free trade reduces the rate of increase of the climatic debt. This is therefore a major advance, in addition to the other advantages exposed by Ricardo. His free trade is good for the climate.

4.2 *Generalized free trade through free movement of capital*

But this beneficial aspect of a lesser release of entropy by free trade does not apply to the case of two countries practicing generalized free trade, including the free movement of capital and people. The reason is that the lower level of nominal wages in the less developed country (in this case Portugal) would become the determining factor for the English capitalist. It is these low wages that induce him to transfer the production of goods manufactured in England to Portugal, since they greatly increase his profit. Generalized free trade will increase the climatic debt, because it is not based on a specialization which would allow each participant to give the best of himself, but only on the easy gain that low nominal wages in Portugal allow. This is what the free movement of capital does.

Contrary to free trade as advocated by Ricardo, generalized free trade does not stimulate industry, does not reward ingenuity, and does not distribute labor in the most effective and economical way. On the contrary, one can even expect that the production of textiles in Portugal will be less efficient than in England, because the workers there are less qualified. In addition, the environmental constraints will be less severe. Ricardo's arguments in favor of free trade restricted to the exchange of goods do not apply to the case of generalized free trade. The efficiency will be lower. It may even be lower than in countries that do not practice free trade at all.

Moreover, free trade including the free movement of capital allows the capitalist to make a profit simply by transferring the know-how developed in England to Portugal, whose lower wages he exploits. It does not encourage progress because it does not promote innovation. In fact, it delays it.

However, it must be recognized that generalized free trade will further increase what Ricardo called "the sum of enjoyments", in the sense that the low wages paid allow the capitalist to put on the market lower-cost products in greater quantities.

All in all, the resulting increase in consumption and less efficient production will lead to an increase in the release of entropy. The free movement of capital will increase CO_2 emissions and the climate debt.

This conclusion, based on a careful reading of Ricardo's text and on the notion of entropy developed by thermodynamics, is in perfect agreement with the dizzying increase in CO_2 emissions that followed the promotion of generalized free trade on a planetary scale. This is what we will show in Chapter 8.

5. Effects of Finitude on Carnot and Ricardo Cycles

Carnot assumes that the temperatures of the hot and cold sources are constant, i.e. they are not affected by heat transfers during the cycle. Such sources obviously do not exist, but Carnot's assumption is reasonable as long as the heat exchanges during a cycle are small compared to the heat capacity of the two sources.

However, if the machine performs a large number of cycles, the assumption of constant temperatures is no longer acceptable. Indeed, as heat is transferred from the hot source to the cold source during repeated cycles, the hot source cools down and the cold source warms up. The temperature difference between the two sources decreases and the efficiency decreases. Eventually, the efficiency tends to zero; the machine stops. This does not mean that the machine is not ideal. As long as the entropy change during each cycle is zero, it is possible in principle to use the total work done to bring back to the hot source all the heat that was transferred to the cold source.

The same remarks apply to Ricardo's cycle. He assumes, without explicitly saying so, that the exchange he makes does not alter the differences between the economies of England and Portugal from which he draws. However, the size of Portuguese and English markets is finite, like Carnot's hot and cold sources. If the cycle described by Ricardo is repeated many times, the English cloth will saturate the Portuguese market and Portuguese wine will saturate the English market. Prices will have to fall, and the merchant's profit (i.e. the return on the exchange) will fall. But if the exchange has been free, it will be possible to turn back the clock. The trader will be able to use the profit he has made to move goods back and forth between the two countries. On the other hand, if the exchange was not free, this reversal is not possible.

6. Is It Possible to go Back in Time?

The Carnot cycle and the Ricardo cycle are perfect cycles. They ignore irreversibility. But no machine is perfect. Economic exchanges are not perfect either. There is no reversible machine, and the ideal free exchange does not exist either.

The cycle that Ricardo invents is an ideal cycle, in the sense that it ignores any mechanism that would diminish the profit allowed by exchange, just as Carnot ignores, for example, the effect of friction on the efficiency of his machine. For example, customs duties are such a mechanism. Basically, the possible benefit of trade lies in the existence of differences between the two economies, just as the difference in temperature between a hot and a cold source allows Carnot's machine to provide work. Free trade allows us to maximize the benefits of foreign trade, in the same way as removing friction would allow to reach the maximum efficiency of an ideal "fire" machine as calculated by Carnot.

This is not possible if the machine is not ideal. If, for example, there is friction, the heat transferred to the cold source cannot be returned to the hot source. This impossibility of a backward movement, i.e. this irreversibility, is the macroscopic consequence of the mechanism of friction on the microscopic scale.

If an external energy source is available, it will be possible to make this backflow, i.e. to make all the heat transferred to the hot source go back to the cold source. It will be necessary to provide to the machine a work equivalent to the one lost because of friction.

Chapter 7

Towards a Major Irreversibility: End of North Pole Glaciation

Because they are irreversible, all the transformations we carry out are accompanied by entropy releases into the environment. CO_2 emissions resulting from the combustion of wood, coal, oil, and gas are but one example. Up a certain threshold, these emissions are compensated by solar energy which recycles CO_2 through photosynthesis. Beyond that threshold, emitted CO_2 molecules keep accumulating. This is what has happened since the beginning of the industrial era, and especially since the 1950s.

1. Is There a Critical Concentration of CO_2?

The current high concentration of CO_2 in the atmosphere is considered to be responsible for the multiplication of already observed extreme climatic effects such as floods, forest fires, and droughts. These effects were predicted about 15 years ago as manifestations of "The Entropy Crisis" (Guy Deutscher, World Scientific, 2008). Since then, the concentration of CO_2 has increased by another 60 ppm and has reached 420 ppm.

IPCC experts are now unanimous in warning governments of the dangers of a continued increase. They continue to emphasize the dangers of warming, and place 1.5 degrees as the limit of an acceptable increase from the beginning of the industrial era. According to the models presented, the increase in temperature depends on the evolution of the CO_2

concentration. The limit of 1.5 degrees could be respected if the emissions were to decrease so that carbon neutrality is reached in 2050. This is the objective set by the COP conferences.

The IPCC report notes an increase in extreme events, which it attributes to global warming. It suggests that these events would be tolerable if the 1.5-degree warming threshold were respected, while acknowledging at the same time that an increase in their frequency and severity is already known.

We are therefore entitled to ask whether a critical threshold of CO_2 concentration has not in fact already been crossed. Placing the limit of warming at 1.5 degrees, within which we would remain in a zone where climate change will remain acceptable, is perhaps the wrong way to approach the issue.

It may be better to stick to the CO_2 concentration itself as a basic parameter. The right question is then to know if there is a threshold of CO_2 concentration beyond which the climate would become irreversibly unstable. If such a threshold exists, where does it lie? Have we already exceeded it? If not, what must be done to prevent it from being crossed? And if the threshold has been crossed, can we go back?

In the previous chapter, we introduced the notion of climate debt: it is the cost of extracting the excess CO_2 from the atmosphere, i.e. the CO_2 that has accumulated since the beginning of the industrial era. It is of the order of the annual GDP of the United States. This cost is so high that large-scale extraction can only be considered if it is essential for our survival on earth, i.e. if the critical concentration threshold has already been reached or is about to be reached.

It is therefore important to evaluate what would be a critical threshold of CO_2 concentration. By this, we mean a threshold beyond which the climate behavior would be irreversibly different from that observed in the past.

2. Climatic Instabilities

Our planet is at the moment the only one known where water exists in liquid form in abundance. This has not always been the case for the planets of the solar system. On Venus, it is thought that water existed in the distant past in liquid form but that it evaporated under the influence of solar radiation. On more distant planets, water still exists in the form of ice. The planet earth, with its large mass of liquid water, is the exception. But is this exception destined to last? It is not certain.

Gorshkov has established that greenhouse gases can affect the stability of the climate. Above a certain concentration, the temperature becomes so high that it is above a critical temperature above which there is no difference between liquid water and vapor. In this state, there is complete evaporation, and water molecules escape from the stratosphere. This would have been the case for Venus on the billion-year scale, due to an increase in solar radiation combined with a high concentration of CO_2.

An evaporation phenomenon could in principle also develop on earth. The concentration of H_2O molecules in the atmosphere increases exponentially with the ocean temperatures. At current temperatures, this concentration is low compared to that of CO_2. But an increase in temperature could trigger a runaway effect, because H_2O molecules very efficiently absorb the infrared radiation re-emitted by the earth: the more the concentration of water vapor increases, the more the greenhouse effect is important, and the more the temperature increases. In the end, all the water evaporates. Conversely, a decrease in temperature can lead to a complete glaciation since it causes a decrease in the concentration of H_2O.

Gorshkov has shown that total evaporation or complete glaciation are the only possible stable states if we stick to the known physical phenomena. He put forward the hypothesis that the stability of the earth's climate, demonstrated by the alternating periods of glaciation and thaw to which we return below, can only be due to biological phenomena. It is life on earth that would ensure its own survival.

Figure 1 shows how a function $U(T)$ represents how the energy of the system varies with temperature at the water–atmosphere interface. The earth would currently be at point 2 which is unstable.

3. Alternating Glacial and Interglacial Periods for the Last Million Years

It is useful to start with a reminder of the evolution of climatic conditions on the scale of the last million years, for which we have very precise data on both CO_2 concentration and temperatures.

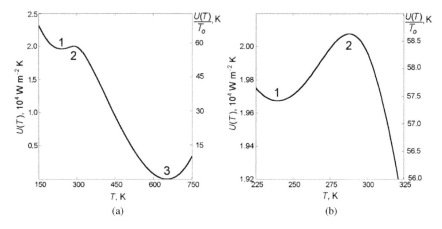

Figure 1.   (a) Points 1 (complete glaciation) and 3 (complete evaporation) are stable. Point 2, which represents the current state of the earth, is unstable. Small fluctuations should bring it to either point 1 or point 3. Such fluctuations have existed over hundreds of thousands of years, and yet the climate has remained stable. The figure to the right has an expended temperature scale (According to V.G. Gorshkov and A.M. Makarieva, Atmospheric and Physics discussions. *European Geosciences Union*, 2002, **2**(2), pp. 2898–3337).

For this period, CO_2 concentration measurements were made on samples taken from very thick ice sheets in the Antarctic continent, which contain air bubbles whose CO_2 content is that of the atmosphere at the time the ice was formed. The cores are dated by measuring the relative concentration of the isotope ^{18}O, which varies with temperature and is quite different in summer and winter. This allows one to count the number of years along a core. The relationship between [18]O concentration and temperature has been established quantitatively, for example, by calibrating it on temperature differences measured simultaneously at different altitudes.

The measured variation of [18]O content allowed one to establish the variation of the temperatures over long periods of times. We thus have precise information on the evolution of the atmospheric CO_2 content over 800,000 years. This method does not work at earlier times because of ice melting due to the heat of the rocks on which it was deposited.

Figure 2 shows the now famous CO_2 quasi-periodic fluctuations whose amplitude is of the order of 100 ppm. It seems that at each

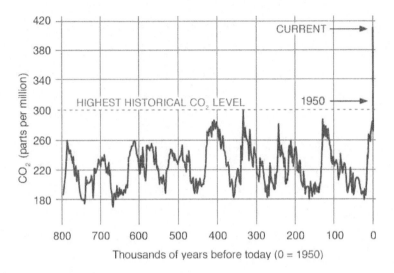

Figure 2. During the last 800,000 years, the atmospheric CO_2 concentration has oscillated between a minimum value of 180 ppm and a maximum value of 300 ppm, reached only once. For the last four cycles, the maximum value was rather 280 ppm. For the last four cycles, the 100,000-year periodicity has been the most pronounced. Each cycle begins with a rapid increase in CO_2 of about 100 ppm over a few thousand years, followed by a gradual decrease.

oscillation a negative feedback mechanism prevents these fluctuations from diverging, and brings the system back to equilibrium. But could this oscillatory regime, possibly a property of the biosphere as proposed by Gorshkov, not be interrupted by the very sudden increase of CO_2 during the last century?

Indeed, on the 800,000-year time scale, the recent increase in CO_2 appears as a vertical line. Its current value, 420 ppm, is much higher than its average value during the period covered by this graph, about 230 ppm. This increase has been so strong and so rapid that one must wonder whether the periodic alternations will persist in the future.

As shown in Figure 3, the changes in CO_2 concentration and temperature are in the same direction and are remarkably synchronized. The temperature oscillations have an amplitude of 8 degrees Celsius. They are the mark of an alternation between glacial periods, where both polar caps are covered with ice, and (shorter) interglacial periods during which only the South Pole (the Antarctic continent) is covered.

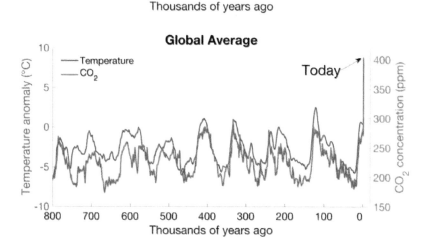

Figure 3. Temperature variations are synchronized with those of CO_2 concentration. This synchronization is visible in the smallest details during the last 400,000 years during which the oscillations are the most regular and clearly dominated by a period of 100,000 years. The perfect synchronization suggests that a single underlying mechanism controls both CO_2 concentration and temperature.

3.1 *Origin of interglacial periods*

Figures 2 and 3 show for the last 800,000 years a succession of interglacial warming. They often begin with a rapid increase in CO_2 and temperature; CO_2 and temperature decline simultaneously and gradually for about 100,000 years. The duration of interglacial periods is variable. The last temperature peak, reached 100,000 years ago, lasted for about 10,000 years and was narrower than that of 400,000 years ago.

The current warming interglacial period started 12,000 years ago. If it follows the same pattern as previous interglacial periods, it should be followed by a progressive decrease in temperature and CO_2 concentration. The North Pole ice sheet should then extend southward, covering a large part of Europe and the North American continent.

In the Milankovitch cycle model, temperature oscillations are due to insolation variations as the eccentricity of earth's orbit (400,000 years periodicity with a modulation of 100,000 years), the inclination of its axis of rotation on the plane of its orbit (41,000 years), the precession of this axis (20,000 years), and the angle that the plane of its orbit makes with the average plane of all the planets (100,000 years) all have periodic changes. The interglacial periods are longer when the eccentricity of the earth's orbit is low. This is now the case as it was 400,000 years ago. The current interglacial period could last for several tens of thousands of years.[1]

The synchronization of CO_2 and temperature variations suggests a common origin; for instance, the amount of CO_2 in the atmosphere depends on the rate at which it is absorbed by photosynthesis. During an ice age, a large part of the land is covered by ice, so this rate is low. As the CO_2 emitted by volcanic discharges accumulates, temperature rises through the greenhouse effect, eventually causing the ice age to end. As the vegetation cover expands, photosynthesis accelerates, CO_2 content decreases again, the greenhouse effect weakens, and temperatures fall.

In detail, many other factors have to be taken into account, such as the change of albedo with the ice cover. However, the consensus is that during the last 800,000 years, oscillations of the insolation are at the origin of those of the temperature and, indirectly, of those of the CO_2 content by a feedback mechanism. During this period, the average concentration of CO_2 in the atmosphere has not changed. It has remained at the level of 230 ppm.

4. Major Ice Ages

The regular succession of glacial and interglacial periods, clearly observed during the last 800,000 years, is a relatively recent phenomenon. It is not

---

[1] A. Berger and F.M. Loutre, *La Recherche* 368, **42** (2003).

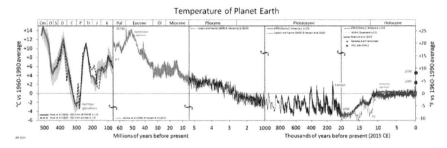

Figure 4.   This montage shows the evolution of temperatures at progressively later times, from the present so-called interglacial period on the right (Holocene) to the largest accessible time scale on the left (Permian). Simultaneous glaciation of the two poles occurred only twice, 300 million years ago and during the last 3 million years (adapted from Inglis Gordon *et al.*, 2015, *Paleoceanography* 30(7), 1000–1020).

representative of the long-term evolution of the climate. On the time scale of hundreds of millions of years, polar glaciation is a rare phenomenon.

For long periods of time, neither pole was covered by ice. As can be seen in Figure 4, there have been only two major ice ages defined as periods of time when both poles are covered by ice. The first one occurred 300 million years ago and a second one started 3 million years ago. During these two periods of major glaciation, the average temperature was the same, from 2 to 4 degrees lower than the current temperature. Most of the time, the temperature was substantially higher than today, typically by 5 to 10 degrees Celsius.

An intermediate ice age, where only the South Pole was covered by ice, began 20 to 40 million years ago. Since then, the temperature has been decreasing continuously, leading to the current major glaciation.

The 5- to 10-degree temperature oscillations that took place during the last 800,000 years are unusual. As can be seen in Figure 4, these oscillations gradually diminish at earlier times. Did large temperature oscillations, up to 10 degrees in amplitude, also occur during the first major ice age 300 million years ago? The time resolution does not allow one to say. However, we notice that at the end of this period the temperature rose rapidly by about 15 degrees. One may wonder whether the strong oscillations observed during the last 800,000 years, and particularly during the last 400,000 years, are the sign of a massive warming to come.

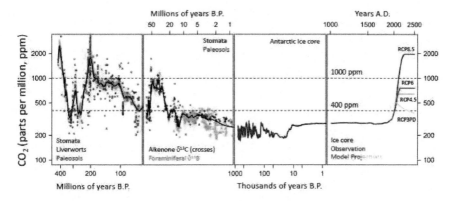

Figure 5. The evolution of the CO_2 concentration is similar to that of the temperature shown in Figure 4. During the two major ice ages, 300 million years ago and the last 3 million years , the concentration is well below 400 ppm (adapted from Glen Fergus C.C. BY-SA 3.0, quoted by Owen Mulhern in "A graphical history of atmospheric CO_2 levels over time").

The current low CO_2 content is also a rare phenomenon. Indeed, one has to go back 300 million years to find a CO_2 content as low as it is today as can be seen in Figure 5.

The evolution of CO_2 content over the last 40 million years is shown in more detail in Figure 6. It can be clearly seen that the drops recorded 25 million years ago and 3 million years ago coincide with those of the temperatures that can be seen in Figure 4.

It is admitted that permanent glaciation of the North Pole, in addition to that of the South Pole, is only possible when the CO_2 content is lower than 270 ppm, while that of the South Pole is possible when it falls below 750 ppm, as shown in Figure 7.

The major glaciations are therefore fundamentally different from the alternation between glacial and interglacial periods of the last million years, because they are controlled by the concentration of CO_2 and not by the periodic variations of insolation.

5. The Last 5 Million Years

On the scale of 5 million years, the evolution of temperatures is shown Figure 8.

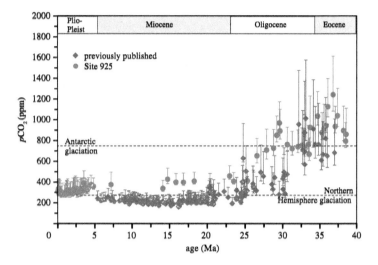

Figure 6.   Evolution of CO_2 content over the last 40 million years. The most recent measurements (in blue) clearly show a drop in two stages, one 25 million years ago and the other 3 million years ago. The first stage coincides with the South Pole glaciation and the second to that of the North Pole. It occurred after the CO_2 concentration dropped below 400 ppm (adapted from Yi-Ge Zhang *et al.*, 2013, *Philosophical Transactions of the Royal Society* A 371, 20130096).

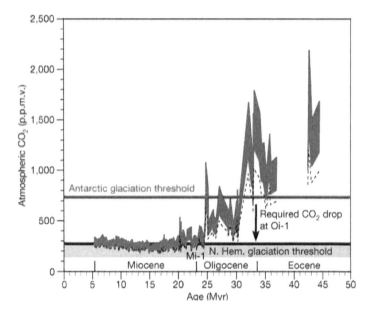

Figure 7.   Antarctic and bi-polar glaciations thresholds (adapted from R.M. Deconto, 2008, *Nature*, 455–652.

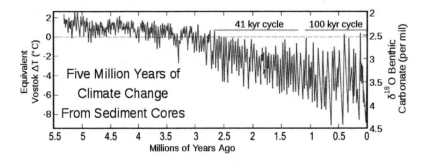

Figure 8. Evolution of the temperature established from the concentration of ^{18}O measured in samples of sedimentary layers that fix their dating (adapted from M. Brunetti and F. Prodi, 2015, *EPJ Web of Conference* 98, 02001).

The average temperature has decreased by about 8 degrees Celsius. It should be noted, however, that during this period the amplitude of the oscillations has gradually increased to reach during the last million years a value of the same order as the decrease of the average values. For the last million years, the oscillations have a dominant periodicity of 100,000 years, as already shown in Figure 3. Up to 1 to 2.5 million years ago, a shorter periodicity of 41,000 years dominates. The amplitude of the oscillations is a little smaller, about 4 degrees. Beyond 3 million years, the temperature does not vary much anymore, and the amplitude of the fluctuations is much smaller, about 1 degree.

There has clearly been a transition between two regimes. More than 5 million years ago, temperatures were controlled by CO_2 concentration, while during the last million years the oscillations of temperature and CO_2 concentration were synchronized by astronomical variations of insolation, as theorized by Milankovitch.

The transition begins with the decrease in temperature about 3 million years ago (Figure 8). As can be seen in more detail in Figure 10(c), this decline corresponds to that of CO_2 2.4 million years ago, when it fell down to 270 ppm. Permanent glaciation of the North Pole then begins (see Figure 6), and temperature oscillations become progressively more pronounced. During the last million years, the average CO_2 concentration has been 230 ppm.

It should be noted, however, that the determination of CO_2 concentration becomes more difficult beyond the 800,000 years during which it was

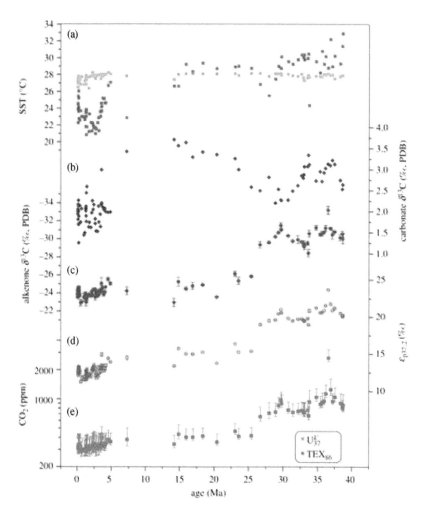

Figure 9. Different methods used for the determination of CO_2 concentration on a 40 million year scale (adapted from Yi-Ge Zhang *et al.*, 2013, *Philosophical Transactions of the Royal Society* A 371, 0130096).

obtained by a direct measurement in the air bubbles remaining trapped in the ice extracted by coring. Beyond that, the determination is more indirect. It is done by methods using different isotopes in plant fossils. The different methods used agree, however, on one important point, namely, that until 2.5 million years ago the concentration of CO_2 did not exceed 400 ppm (see Figure 9).

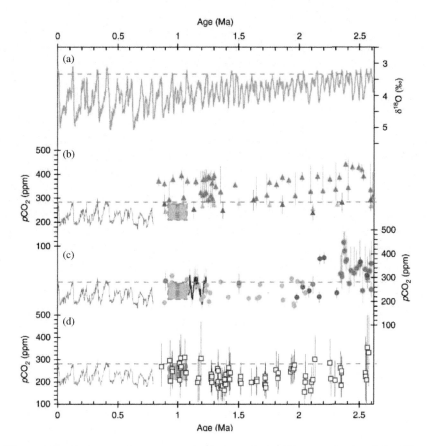

Figure 10. Evolution of temperature and atmospheric CO_2 over the last 2.6 million years: (a) isotope concentration ^{18}O, a proxy for temperature; (b, c, and d) atmospheric CO_2. The most recent measurements (c) and (d) show that the average CO_2 concentration remained roughly constant at the 230 ppm level until 2.4 million years ago. The horizontal line marks the value of 270 ppm above which complete glaciation of the North Pole is not possible according to current climate models (adapted from Jiawei Da, Yi Ge Zhang, Gen Li, Xiangiang Meng and Junfeng Ji, 2019, *Nature Communications* 10, 4342).

6. Current Interglacial Period: Consequences of the Massive CO_2 Release

The addition of 140 ppm of CO_2 since the beginning of the industrial era has increased the concentration from 280 to 420 ppm in one century. Even if we assume that anthropogenic CO_2 emissions stop immediately and that oscillations of 100 ppm will continue in the future, we arrive at a value of 370 ppm averaged over the duration of a glacial–interglacial cycle. In the most optimistic scenario currently considered, carbon neutrality would not actually be reached until 2050. Assuming that the rate of increase goes linearly from the current value of 3.5 ppm per year to zero in 2050, the concentration would then reach the value of 450 ppm. Whatever the assumptions made, the CO_2 level is well above the 270 ppm required for permanent glaciation of the North Pole, and takes us back more than 20 million years to a time when temperatures were 4 degrees higher than today.

In any case, any concentration above 400 ppm is incompatible with a North Pole glaciation; see Figure 6. This value is already clearly exceeded, and will be even more widely exceeded in 2050. Therefore, even in the most optimistic scenario, all North Pole ice is doomed to disappear. There will be no more alternation between glacial and interglacial periods as has been the case during the last 800,000 years.

This conclusion, based on climate models combined with determinations of CO_2 concentration at times millions of years ago, is consistent with measurements of Arctic ice volume change in recent years. Detailed measurements since 1980, shown in Figure 11, indicate that this volume began to decrease from about 1990, when the CO_2 concentration was 350 ppm. These observations directly confirm that above this concentration the Arctic ice is doomed to disappear completely. On the basis of these measurements, we can predict that there will be no more Arctic ice in summer by 2040, and no ice at all by the end of this century.

Current and projected CO_2 levels mark a return to conditions that prevailed more than 5 million years ago, before the North Pole glaciation started. These dramatic conclusions would only be challenged if CO_2 levels fell below 300 ppm quickly enough.

We have here the answer to the question we asked in the previous chapter:

Is there a critical value of CO_2 concentration above which drastic climate change would occur, and if so what is it; has it already been exceeded or can we still avoid it?

According to the recent work (less than 20 years) that we have cited above, the answer is that this critical value, according to different sources,

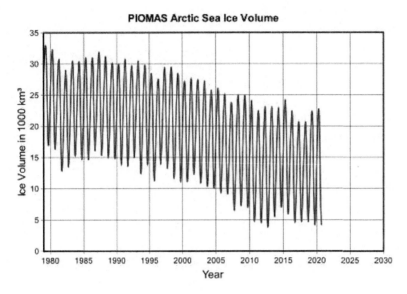

PIOMAS Arctic Sea Ice Volume

Figure 11. Decrease in Arctic ice volume, visible since 1990. At the current rate, the summer ice cover should disappear by 2040 and the winter ice cover by the end of the 21st century. About half of it has already disappeared since 1980.

lies between 300 and 400 ppm, and has already been crossed. Even if we were to drastically reduce our CO_2 emissions, we would not prevent the Arctic ice from melting. As shown in Figure 11, it is now starting to melt, at a rate of 500 km^3 /year, or about 500 Gt/year.

6.1 *CO_2 residence time and dynamics of glacier melting*

There is, however an important element that we did not take into account, namely, the residence time of anthropogenic CO_2. This residence time is to be compared to the time needed for glaciers melting. Our conclusions are valid only if the residence time is the longer one. In this case, the North Pole ice will have effectively melted before the excess CO_2 has been absorbed.

CO_2 released in the atmosphere is gradually resorbed by several mechanisms. Some are fast, like dissolution in the ocean and photosynthesis. Others are much slower, like the formation of sedimentary carbonates.

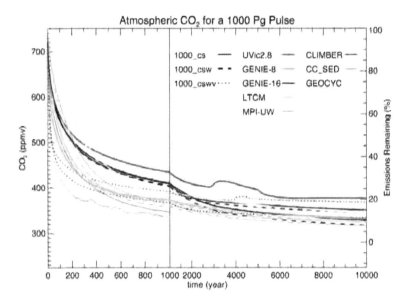

Figure 12. CO_2 decay after an injection of 1,000 pentagrams (1,000 gigatons). The dotted curves correspond to models (cswv notes) that take into account both fast mechanisms (such as dissolution in the oceans) and slow mechanisms (carbonate formation and sedimentation) (David Archer *et al.* 2009, Atmospheric life time of fossil-fuel carbon dioxide. In *Annual Review of Earth and Planetary Sciences* 37; see also David Archer. 2005, *Journal of Geophysical Research* 110, C09S05).

Therefore, as shown Figure 12, one cannot characterize the decrease in CO_2 concentration after a rapid injection by a single decay time. Very schematically, 50% of the injected CO_2 is resorbed rapidly, on the scale of a few years; another 30% is resorbed after a few centuries, and the remaining 20% remains in the atmosphere on the scale of 10,000 years.

In total, CO_2 released since the beginning of the industrial era amounts to 1,000 pentagrams or 1,000 gigatons (1 pentagram is 1 gigaton; annual releases are about 40 gigatons). The results of several models of the decay of atmospheric CO_2 following the injection of 1,000 petragrams are shown in Figure 11. This injection causes an instantaneous increase in concentration from 270 ppm to 750 ppm. The decay is very rapid at short times, but after 1,000 years the concentration is still well above 350 ppm.

7. Ice Melting: Arctic in 100 Years and Greenland in 1000 Years

Our conclusion is that melting of Arctic ice is indeed inevitable, even without any additional emissions. The decay of the Arctic ice mass, now well established (Fig. 11), is not a temporary phenomenon. It will continue until its final disappearance, probably by the end of the century.

Arctic ice is only a fraction of the Northern Hemisphere ice. The most important ice mass is found in Greenland. Measurements since the early 2000s show that it is also decreasing, by about 250 Gt/year (Figure 13). The Greenland ice is melting slightly faster than the polar ice. But the big difference lies in its mass. The mass of Greenland ice is about 5 million Gigatons, compared to the 20,000 Gt mass of Arctic ice. At the present rate, it will take more than a thousand years to melt. But since, as we have

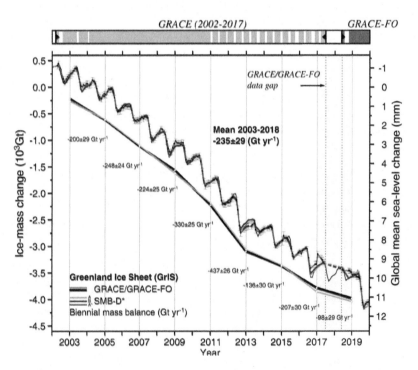

Figure 13. Melting of the Greenland ice, noticeable since the early 2000s. It will persist much longer than Arctic ice, for more than a thousand years at the current rate.

seen, at this time scale the concentration of atmospheric CO_2 will still be above 350 ppm, even without any additional emissions, Greenland ice is also set to disappear. As for the Antarctic ice, its mass is estimated at 26 million Gigatons. The current and predicted concentrations of CO_2 are below the 750 ppm required for South Pole ice melting.

Melting of the North Hemisphere's ice will be the visible manifestation of a backward movement in time of more than three million years. Measures currently recommended by the international bodies are limited to stopping CO_2 emissions.

They will be insufficient to prevent ice melting because the critical concentration of CO_2 has already been exceeded and, as we have shown, it will remain so for 1,000 years even if we immediately stop any net release of CO_2. The critical point has been crossed about twenty years ago.

The only way to prevent melting of the North Hemisphere ice is to eliminate it. But this will only allow a reversal of the situation if simultaneously additional CO_2 emissions are stopped.

This calls into question the economic policy of generalized free trade that has prevailed since the Second World War, and especially since the beginning of the 1990s. This brings us back to our central point, namely, that resolution of the current impasse will only be possible through the active collaboration of the scientific and economic communities.

An interesting and important question is whether there is a link between financial debt, an economic tool, and climate debt. In other words, is there a causal link between debt issuance, for instance, by central bankers, and increased CO_2 emissions? We will examine this question in the next chapter.

But one thing is certain: all the explanations provided by central bankers to justify their debt issuance policy can do nothing against the laws of nature, which are known since Carnot, Clausius, and Boltzmann.

Chapter 8

Growth without Innovation: A Disaster for the Climate

Scientists, through their IPCC reports, have been alerting their governments for several years to the danger that the high concentration of CO_2 poses to the climate. At the beginning, they focused on the century-long warming. More recently, they have noted the increasing frequency and magnitude of extreme weather events, such as droughts, floods, and destructive tornadoes. These events seem to escape any useful prediction, even on the scale of a few days or even a few hours. Nevertheless, the high concentration of CO_2 is now considered to be the cause of both the warming, a long-term threat, and of the extreme events that are already present.

It is undeniable that this high concentration is the result of the strong economic growth that we have experienced since the beginning of the 1950s. This growth was wanted by the economists, who set up for this purpose the GATT agreements of 1947. Their implementation has indeed contributed to the acceleration of growth, to the acceleration of energy production, to the acceleration of CO_2 emissions, and (with a slight delay) to the abnormal increase of temperatures. The dire warnings of scientists are now indirectly challenging this economic policy. Major irreversible transformations are taking place before our eyes o n a global scale. The IPCC experts do not directly question growth, but it is indeed growth that is targeted by their work, and through it the free trade policy.

However, economists, for their part, continue to affirm that economic growth is indispensable to improve the lot of the billions of people who have not yet been able to benefit from the progress made possible by the economic policy of openness carried out since the Second World War under their aegis. From their point of view, it is imperative to continue with it. It is unthinkable to question free trade policy. It would therefore be up to scientists to develop the techniques that will allow us to continue to grow while reducing CO_2 emissions in the atmosphere. But to what extent is this possible?

Until now, in the absence of a direct and constructive discussion between scientists and economists, which would make it possible to lay the foundations of a policy that would take into account both the need for continued growth and the limits imposed by the preservation of our environment, governments are subject to the pressures of various political groups that are not bothered by the contingencies imposed by the laws of nature. Monumental mistakes are thus made, such as the premature abandonment of nuclear energy in countries where it was already well established and erratic investments in emerging countries, often destructive of their environment.

A dialogue between scientists and economists is necessary and urgent.

1. 1950: A Pivotal Year

It can be said that scientists and economists agree on one essential point: the growth mode we have known since the 1950s is not sustainable. It may even have already led to irreversible changes in the climate. For example, as we have shown in the previous chapter, the regular alternation between glacial and inter-glacial periods, which has been the hallmark of the climatic order of the last million years, is unlikely to recur. The current concentration of CO_2, over 420 ppm, is such that a new glaciation of the northern hemisphere is no longer possible. The disappearance of the ice pack is now inevitable. Its consequences are largely unpredictable.

1.1 *Simultaneous increases in population, energy consumption and emissions CO_2*

To shed light on the mechanism that led to this untenable situation, it is instructive to compare on a global scale the increase in population

World population by region

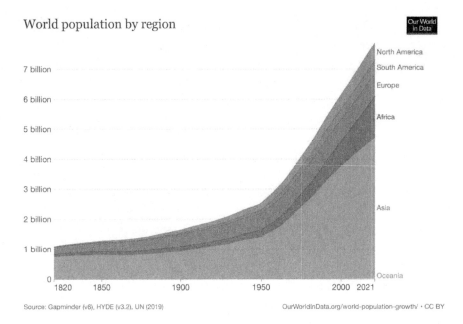

Source: Gapminder (v6), HYDE (v3.2), UN (2019)   OurWorldInData.org/world-population-growth/ • CC BY

Figure 1.   The world's population has been growing faster since 1950, with most of this growth occurring in Asia, but the fastest growth has been in Africa.

(Figure 1), the increase in energy consumption (which closely follows the increase in Gross Domestic Product) (Figure 2), and the increase in CO_2 emissions (Figure 3). In all three cases, the increase becomes more rapid from 1950 onwards, which appears to be a turning point year. The population has tripled since 1950, driven by Asian and African populations. Energy consumption has increased even faster, by a factor of 8, as has the Gross National Product. On average, per capita energy consumption has increased by almost a factor of 3. CO_2 emissions have followed energy consumption.

1.2 *The views of economists and scientists*

Economists rejoiced at this rapid growth, since the increase in population and its purchasing power can rightly be credited to the free trade policy promoted by the GATT agreements. Signed in 1947, they were followed by a rapid increase in international trade, as shown in Figure 1 of Chapter 5.

Global primary energy consumption by source

Primary energy is calculated based on the 'substitution method' which takes account of the inefficiencies in fossil fuel production by converting non-fossil energy into the energy inputs required if they had the same conversion losses as fossil fuels.

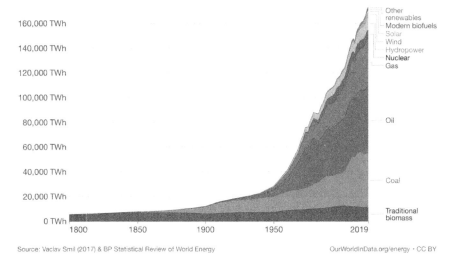

Source: Vaclav Smil (2017) & BP Statistical Review of World Energy   OurWorldInData.org/energy · CC BY

Figure 2.   Energy consumption increases rapidly after 1950, but its primary sources vary little. They remain largely dominated by conventional energy sources, fossil fuels, and hydropower. The contribution of nuclear energy is still minor, and that of solar and wind power has been negligible until now.

But scientists are now concerned because growth has been fueled by the same energy sources as before. As can be seen in Figure 2, the share of fossil fuels in energy production has remained largely dominant. Truly new energies, i.e. those developed since 1950 — nuclear, solar, and wind — still account for only a few percent of total energy production. Hydro power is certainly non-polluting, but it is not new.

2. Growth Since the GATT Agreements: An Economic Success, a Failure for the Planet

The increase in the use of fossil fuels to meet the needs generated by free trade has been meteoric, as shown in Figure 3. It marks a major failure of economic policy, since it has resulted in a massive increase in the CO_2 content of the atmosphere.

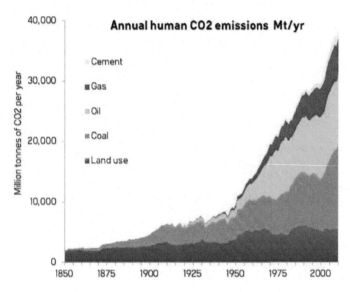

Figure 3. CO_2 emissions since the beginning of the industrial era. Emissions increase moderately until 1950, then more rapidly with the massive use of oil. The increase in emissions from coal has accelerated recently.

2.1 *The measurements of the Mauna Loa Observatory*

It has been measured regularly, day after day, since 1958, by the Mauna Loa laboratory located in Hawaii, far from any source of pollution. These measurements, shown in Figure 4, are representative of the atmospheric CO_2 content on a global scale. In 1958, it was 315 ppm; in 2022, it has reached 420 ppm. These figures are to be compared with the range of 180 to 280 ppm in which the concentration has remained for the last million years. In 1950, it was still only a little higher than normal, nothing very alarming. But in 2022, it reached the value it had more than 3 million years ago and has, according to recent work, now exceeded the limit beyond which an ice age of the northern hemisphere is no longer possible, 270 ppm; see Figure 7 of Chapter 4.

North Pole ice is now doomed to disappear, even if we stop all additional CO_2 emissions immediately. At the current rate of emissions, the threshold above which the South Pole would also become unglaciated, about 700 ppm, might even be reached in a century.

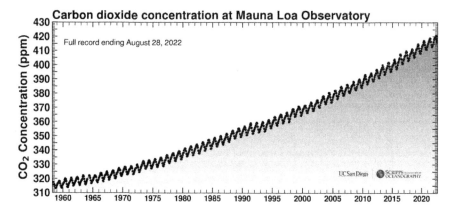

Figure 4.   Evolution of CO_2 concentration measured at the Mauna Loa Observatory since 1958. Its increase has not ceased to accelerate, despite the commitments of the signatory countries of the agreements concluded at the COP conferences.

2.2 *The temperature increase*

The pronounced increase in CO_2 emissions since 1950, Figure 3, which is a direct result of the increase in energy consumption, is reflected in the increase in temperatures. Figure 5 shows how the global average surface temperature has evolved since 1880, with the zero of the temperature scale corresponding to the average over the period 1900–2000. After oscillating from 1880 to 1960, the average temperature has steadily increased. Since 1970, it has increased at a rate of 2 degrees per century.

3. The Impact of Generalized Free Trade on Global Warming and Climate Change

It is clear that the global free trade policy has triggered the rapid growth of energy consumption since 1950 and with it global warming.

This has happened because growth has been fueled by the same conventional energy resources as before: coal, oil, and gas. It is the lack of significant innovation in energy production methods that has led to the climate change we see today. It is not the growth itself that is at fault, but the method by which it was obtained.

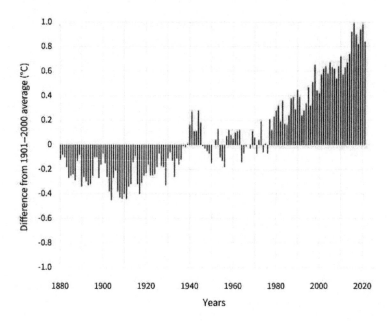

Figure 5. Global average surface temperatures compared to the average temperature from 1901 to 2000. Since 1970, the increase has been continuous.

3.1 *Free trade and lack of innovation*

Lack of innovation in energy production is flagrant. It is paradoxical, since according to Ricardo, free trade is supposed to favor innovation. How can this be explained? Let us recall once more that according to Ricardo the virtue of free exchange is that it allows one to reach the same production level with fewer working days, precisely because it favors the most ingenious and inventive entrepreneurs. For the same reasons, it should have favored the less-energy- and raw-material-intensive production methods. But this did not happen.

We believe that it is the free movement of capital that has distorted the basic mechanism of free trade.

As discussed in Chapter 5, free trade agreements involving free movement of capital have become the majority with China's entry into the World Trade Organization. Since then, free capital movement has lowered production costs and accelerated growth, as desired. But it has done so by the transfer of known production processes to low-wage countries rather than by developing new technologies.

3.2 *The absence of innovation; consequence of a harmful combination of free trade in goods and free movement of capital*

Relocation requires initial investments. These investments could be made thanks to the free circulation of capital (from rich countries to developing countries), while free trade allowed the export of the production of the delocalized factory, without duties. Thanks to the lower wages paid in developing countries, goods produced in delocalized factories could successfully compete with localized production.

The owners of capital have thus realized greater profits simply by replicating the known processes and know-how developed in the rich countries. Production growth was possible without innovation, using the same processes and the same sources of energy. This explains why economic growth and CO_2 emissions have increased at exactly the same rate.

In our opinion, the generalization of free movement of capital, without any discrimination or control, has done away with the benefits of the original free trade, practiced without free movement of capital, as described by Ricardo. If no significant progress has been made in the field of the use of natural resources and labor for industrial production, it is because the owners of capital were able to make it fructify faster by relocating their production tools to low-cost countries than by investing in innovation.

Instead of encouraging innovation and excellency, generalized free trade has promoted technological stagnation from 1950 to 2020. This is not surprising. The engine of free trade has always been profit, not the common good. Without free movement of capital, the two are compatible, that is the known liberal theory. But with an indiscriminate free flow of capital, they are not, since profits can increase through delocalization of industrial production to low-wage countries, without significant innovation.

3.3 *Transfer of polluting industries to low-wage countries*

Generalized free trade has led to the massive transfer of traditional industries, which are also the most polluting ones, to low-wage countries. These industries, such as metallurgy, certain chemical industries, the textile industry, and its dyes, employ a large workforce. With few exceptions, they have basically disappeared from the countries where they had been developed.

The lower cost of production has brought down prices and thus increased consumption. In addition, less severe regulations aimed at limiting impact on the environment have increased all polluting emissions, including CO_2 by a massive use of coal, more polluting than other fossil fuel sources.

Table 1 shows the evolution of steel production from 1967 to 2021. As can be seen, this production has been dramatically shifted from Western countries to Asia.

China is obviously the most striking example, but it is not the only one to have seen its share of production increase. Together, China, India, Japan, and South Korea now account for two-third of the world's steel production.

Steel is generally used locally for the production of finished products. The transfer of steel production is accompanied by a much wider transfer of industrial production.

The shift in industrial production during the same period is also apparent when comparing changes in coal production; see Figure 6. Here again, 1950 appears to be a pivotal year. China's production becomes significant, while that of France and the United Kingdom begins to decline. Another important year is the year 2000, when US coal consumption, until then quite robust, starts to decline rapidly. In 2000, the US and

Table 1.   Steel production in millions of tons.

	World	China	India	Japan	USA	South Korea	Germany
1967	497	14	6.3	62	115	0.3	41.3
2021	1,951	995	118	96	85	70.4	40.1

Coal production

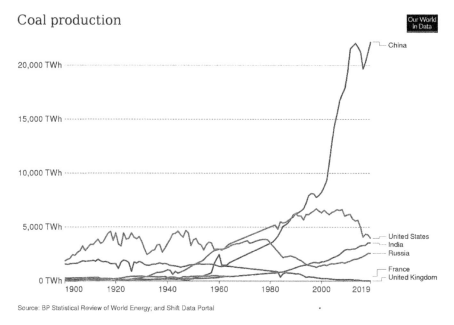

Source: BP Statistical Review of World Energy; and Shift Data Portal

Figure 6. Comparative trends in coal production between China and other industrial countries. This comparison illustrates how quickly China has become the world's leading industrial power in 20 years.

Chinese productions are still close to each other, but in 2019 Chinese production is 5 times higher than American production, in spite of the fact that American coal reserves exceed those of China.

This is indeed a transfer made for reasons of economic profitability: the low wages paid to Chinese workers have made their products more competitive. The graphs we have shown illustrate their dominance in the conventional heavy industry of coal and steel. But this domination is more general, applying to all areas where nominal wages play a decisive role.

This is the origin of the current climate crisis. Low-wage costs have allowed Chinese and other Asian manufacturers to lower their selling prices and to flood the Western markets with cheap consumer products. This was originally done without innovation and led to an increase in CO_2 emissions, which were simply proportional to growth. This growth has been multiplied by the practice of free trade with free movement of capital.

4. Increase of Entropy

Entropy plays an essential role in the climate change caused by the increase of CO_2 emissions. Measurements of CO_2 concentration in different parts of the world show that it is the same everywhere, i.e. the molecules lose the memory of where they were emitted very quickly. Whatever their origin, they will affect the whole atmosphere in a uniform way. Even if the emissions are local, their effect is global. This is why they affect the climate.

The homogeneity of the concentration of CO_2 molecules reflects a fundamental law of physics, due to Boltzmann. Their diffusion increases the entropy of the system by exploring the very large number of possible equivalent locations in the atmosphere, and this entropy increase lowers the free energy of the atmosphere. It is therefore favored. We refer the reader back to Chapters 3 and 4 for an introduction to the Boltzmann and Clausius theories.

As we proposed earlier, the origin of the climate crisis is entropic (see "The Entropy Crisis"). The molecules of CO_2 and other pollutants have spread; their homogeneous distribution has increased the entropy of the biosphere. In the long run, this causes warming and in a more general and immediate way disorder.

4.1 *From global warming to climate disorder*

In recent years, more frequent extreme events like droughts, floods, or tornados have been an increasing cause of concern. In the short term, they are more dangerous than global warming. Are the two phenomena related, and if they are, how?

It is only since the end of the 1980s that scientists have become certain that there is indeed climate warming. The Rio Summit (1992) gave rise to a series of COP conferences (Conference Of Parties, the first of which was organized by Germany in 1995), the aim of which is to agree on the measures to be taken to prevent climate change. The causal link between CO_2 emissions and climate warming is considered to be established, but the means to be used to eliminate these emissions without damaging growth are left to the discretion of the signatory countries.

From the years 1980–1990 onwards, a simple linear extrapolation of the CO_2 concentration measurements at the Mauna Loa Observatory (Figure 4) lends for 2020 a concentration of about 400 ppm of CO_2. In reality the rate of increase of CO_2 concentration has increased even more; we are already at 420 ppm. The recommendations made at successive COP conferences have been ineffective so far. Among the different scenarios considered by the IPCC concerning the evolution of CO_2 emissions, the most pessimistic ones seem to be coming true.

Were the consequences of this high concentration predictable? As far as the average warming is concerned, no doubt, because the models linking the evolution of average temperatures to the CO_2 concentration are well established and have not changed much.

In contrast, models linking CO_2 levels, Arctic ice melt, and more general ice ages, and their comparison with geological data (Deconto *et al.*, 2008, *Nature* 455, 652), are recent. They predict the disappearance of major ice ages in the Northern Hemisphere when CO_2 levels exceed 280 ppm. According to these models, at the current level of 420 ppm, its eventual deglaciation is assured, as we proposed in Chapter 7. Most of the alpine glaciers as well as the arctic ice pack will disappear.

Recently, attention has focused on Greenland deglaciation because of its impact on sea levels. Recent simulations predict a meter-scale rise due mainly to melting of the ice sheet in western Greenland, which would be less stable (Keisling *et al.*, 2022, EarthArXiv). Time scales are still uncertain.

Up to now, the models presented have only been quantitative with respect to average global values, which evolve slowly. They do not include any quantitative prediction of deviations from the mean, either in terms of amplitude and frequency of extreme events, or in terms of their location. However, it seems that deviations from the mean, in their various forms, constitute serious dangers and may cause serious damage. These events are now the focus of attention, rather than average warming or even sea level rise.

It is now accepted that the number and intensity of extreme events are increasing. But meteorological models are not yet able to predict in a useful way when and where droughts, floods, and heat waves will occur. What we see are large fluctuations that make average values unhelpful — they are the hallmark of climate disorder. For example, precipitation remains on average the same on a global scale, but its intensity varies from one region to another. Extreme drought on the one hand and catastrophic floods on the other. But where and when they will occur, meteorologists cannot tell us in advance.

This should come as no surprise, as the effects of entropic disorder are unpredictable.

It is essential to understand and accept that the nature of the current crisis is entropic. It is not a crisis triggered by the depletion of fossil fuel reserves, as the Club of Rome predicted. They are still abundant, especially coal reserves. This is acknowledged by the COP conferences which recommend to stop their exploitation. It is now implicitly admitted that what is at hand is not an energy crisis. What is it about, if not entropy?

This immediately explains why the multiplication of extreme events and their severity are already being felt, while the increase in average temperatures and the rise in sea level are still moderate and do not represent an immediate threat.

The time scales of disorder and warming are indeed different. Disorder, i.e. entropy, follows immediately after the increase in CO_2 concentration — it is proportional to it. On the other hand, warming appears with delay, because of the enormous heat capacity of the biosphere. We must add that ice melting slows down warming because it turns into water at a constant temperature. Seeing glaciers fall apart is frightening. On the other, their melting helps keep down the rise in temperature. But for how long?

The measured (and calculated) average warming is a rather poor indicator of the impact of the CO_2 level on climate disorder. Contrary to what is often claimed, it is not warming that creates extreme events. There are better indicators of climate disorder. Warming is easier to calculate and predict, but in the end not very useful to understand the changes we are undergoing now. Unfortunately, the prediction of extreme events is much more difficult than the prediction of the average evolution. It may be that it is currently out of our reach.

For some reason, the IPCC experts do not use the right word, entropy. Disregarding the teachings of Clausius, they limit themselves to the word energy. This is a mistake, because it blocks any intelligent discussion.

Maybe IPCC experts do not use the word because they are afraid that people in government will not understand it, because by and large they do not know what it is.

4.2 *Lack of innovation and climate disorder*

It is the lack of innovation during a period of rapid growth that is at the origin of the current crisis; see Figures 2 and 3. Without innovation, the increase in CO_2 concentration has inevitably followed the increase in industrial production. The latter was boosted by the free trade policy established energetically after the Second World War, as shown by the coincidence between the GATT agreements and the start of the rapid growth of energy consumption in 1950. It was indeed predictable. We have given an overview of its consequences, many of which are still poorly understood.

Let's say it again, it is not growth itself that is at fault. We should not deduce from the current crisis that degrowth is the solution, and even less that innovation is to be banished. We need to admit that growth can only be sustainable if it is based on innovation. Unfortunately, it has been based on the exploitation of low wages in emerging countries.

This has led to the massive use of fossil fuels. One could even argue that the exploitation of low wages to achieve lower prices has prevented innovation. The negative effect of this exploitation, made possible by the free movement of capital, has outweighed the positive effect of free trade limited to goods and services. This is what emerges from the data shown in Figures 2–4.

Chapter 9

Growth with Innovation: The Way Forward

Since the Second World War, growth has been largely achieved without innovation, and even at its expense. But history gives us many examples of periods of growth based on innovations, such as the development of the steam engine which is at the origin of the industrial revolution, as we have discussed at length.

1. The Basis for a Dialogue between Economists and Scientists

Let us not forget that the concept of the exploitation of differences was developed independently and simultaneously by Ricardo and Carnot at the beginning of the industrial era. While Ricardo demonstrated that the exchange of goods and services between countries with different resources and know-how can improve the overall performance of their economies, Carnot demonstrated that the steam engine provided labor by exploiting the temperature difference between hot and cold sources. In both cases, the greater the differences, the greater the benefits. This exploitation of differences requires ingenuity and innovation.

But this positive scenario has been sidetracked by the exploitation of low wages to boost growth. The vast majority of economists had not foreseen its harmful consequences. This exploitation was made possible by the free movement of capital incorporated into free trade agreements. It has indeed accelerated growth. But at the same time, it has undermined the overall performance of the participating countries because it has discouraged rather than encouraged innovation. However, not all economists have been blind. As we recalled, Maurice Allais, Nobel Prize winner, has been speaking out against excessive globalization since the 1990s. He specifically denounced the objective of a total liberalization of the movement of goods, services, and capital on a world scale, initiated by the WTO and developed by the GATT agreements and later within the framework of the WTO. Despite his fame, Maurice Allais's recommendations have been completely ignored.

His opposition to globalization was above all social in nature. He pointed out that every consumer is also a worker. If the consumer benefits from low prices, the worker risks losing his job. He denounced in advance the disorders that would result from globalization in areas where jobs would be lost, such as the suburbs of large cities. History has, unfortunately, proved him right.

The link between economics and physics is clear: the higher growth and the lower efficiency generated by the exploitation of low wages have increased the release of entropy and accelerated the deterioration of the climate.

Maurice Allais did not foresee this consequence that globalization would have on the climate. This is not surprising because it is only in the 1990s that climate change has become clear. Today, we can only observe that the policy of complete liberalization of the economy has created both the climate and the social disorder that Allais had denounced. His opposition to this liberalization is even more grounded than he knew.

2. For a Better Practice of Free Exchange that Favors Innovation

The benefits of free trade, however, cannot be ignored. It should be pursued when it is practiced in such a way as to encourage ingenuity and innovation. Closing borders to international trade is not a good idea, neither is a global ban on the free movement of capital. It too can be practiced in a way that encourages innovation.

This is where a fruitful collaboration between economists and scientists is desirable and possible.

It is important for economists to understand that one material cannot always be replaced by another, and one type of engineer for another. And it is important that scientists accept the virtues of free exchange, that is, the competition of ideas and technologies. Every scientist is convinced that his method is the best. He is not always right. For example, Edison was convinced that direct current was superior to alternating current. As we know, he was wrong and Tesla was right. But Tesla went broke. He was not rewarded for his genius and died in misery. Innovation is a complicated and risky thing. If Westinghouse had not bought Tesla's patents for a symbolic dollar, and if it had not kept his word by exploiting them as he had promised to Tesla, our daily lives might not be what they are today.

On the contrary, the massive investments made to allow for the cheaper manufacture of conventional products by exploiting the low wages of emerging countries have just created disorder.

This does not mean that the free movement of capital is to be proscribed. On the contrary, if practiced with discernment, it can be a great help in promoting innovation. It is even essential.

Traditional free exchange promotes greater efficiency by exploiting existing differences. But, as in Carnot's machine, the differences diminish over time. Carnot's machine will stop, as will trade and growth, for lack of differences.

This is the essential role of innovation. It creates differences, where there were none. And it becomes possible to restart the machine. Without Tesla, and without Westinghouse, electric power would have remained local because it does not allow the transport of electric power over long distances. Alternating current does. This is why it has revolutionized our society, and continues to do so. The fraction of energy consumed in electrical form continues to increase.

But how can we know in advance if a new invention will actually create differences that can be successfully exploited?

2.1 *Innovations in progress to solve the climate disorder*

In the last 60 years, there have been few innovations that have benefited the climate. This is the problem. In the fields of heavy industry like metallurgy and chemistry, in the building industry, in the transport industry, and in the residential heating industry, we are using mostly the same materials and methods as we did 50 years ago. For the most part, we are still producing electricity by burning fossil fuels. Our high furnaces, our mills, our airplanes, our cars, our trains, our ships, our public and private buildings, and our household appliances are still the same. But let us also recognize that there have also been innovative developments.

An important one has been nuclear energy, but it too is more than 50 years old. Moreover, after a promising start, it became increasingly unpopular because of safety concerns including the disposal of long-lived radioactive waste. The latest generation of EPR reactors has the potential to improve public acceptance. The current crisis has also highlighted the value of nuclear energy as a source of carbon-free energy. Originally, however, this had not been the reason for its development, but rather the fear of an upcoming depletion of fossil fuels, the famous peak oil which has so far not materialized. Now, it is the strong desire for carbon-free energy that is driving renewed interest in nuclear energy. But uranium resources are themselves limited and insufficient for a widespread implementation of current reactors. More research is needed to develop, for instance, breeder reactors.

Nuclear fusion still holds the promise of unlimited power supply, but progress has been slow. Tokamak-type reactors burn a mixture of Deuterium and Tritium. Fusion is carried out in a high-temperature plasma confined by intense magnetic fields produced by large superconducting coils, cooled down to a few degrees above absolute zero. The vicinity of very high and very low temperatures is technologically challenging. But superconducting coils are the only practical way to produce intense magnetic fields in large volumes. Wires are made of materials discovered in the seventies, but it has taken many years of effort to bring them up to the level required for the fabrication of large coils.

The ITER fusion project is based on them. The first plasma ignition was planned for the end of 2025, but is being delayed to 2030. A further

DEMO model should provide 500 MW, with 50 MW being necessary to heat the plasma. Sufficient supply of Tritium is not ensured. Even in the case of success of ITER and the following DEMO, we are still very far from a commercial operation. It may not happen before the end of this century.

The use of photovoltaic (PV) panels has become widespread. They were originally developed for space application for which cost was not an issue. Since the early seventies, when their use as terrestrial power sources on earth was first considered seriously because of the fear of an oil shortage, much progress has been done. Production costs have come down by two orders of magnitude; the conversion efficiency of commercial modules now exceeds 20%. Without being revolutionary, since the fundamental physics and the materials used remain the same as they were 50 years ago, this technology is a great success. New materials and production methods were explored actively to achieve lower costs and higher conversion efficiencies. But for the time being, single crystal silicon technology, the first to be exploited, has won out. Surprisingly, the Chinese industry has succeeded in lowering production costs to such an extent that the price of solar modules is no longer an obstacle to their massive deployment. This is a sensational success.

In 2021, installed PV power reached 800 GW; see Figure 1. It is now the fastest growing renewable non-carbon energy source, at a rate of 150 GW/year. Installed wind power is now at the same level as solar, but growing more slowly at a rate of 50 GW/year. These remarkable advances are not yet decisive in the absence of marketable storage of the electricity produced, but a comparison with installed nuclear power is nevertheless interesting. It is now of about 450 GW worldwide. Taking into account the more limited capacity factor of solar and wind, around 20% to 30% compared to 80% or more for nuclear, powers delivered by solar and wind on the one hand and nuclear on the other are today roughly equivalent. But renewables, particularly solar, are growing faster.

So far, there has been no decisive innovation for large-scale energy storage, the only way to make maximum use of intermittent renewables. Storage in the form of hydrogen obtained by electrolysis of water remains to be implemented on an industrial scale.

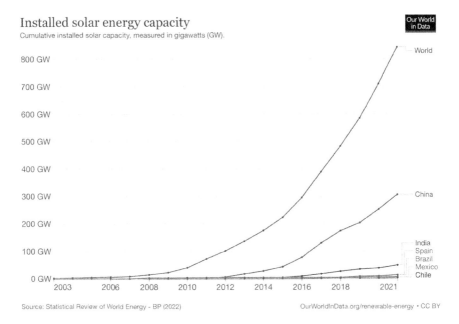

Figure 1.   Growth of installed PV power has been fast since the early 2000s. China uses only part of the PV modules it produces. It is expected that by 2025, 95% of PV modules will be produced in China.

They have been few innovations in the field of transportation. Ships, trains, and airplanes still consume as much energy, and emit as much CO_2, as they did decades ago. The electric car is not really revolutionary. It will reduce air pollution in urban and peri-urban areas, but will not contribute to reducing CO_2 emission unless electricity is supplied from decarbonated sources.

Superconductors today offer the possibility of a real innovation in energy production. They are already the basis of the ITER project. The new High-Temperature ceramic (HTS) superconductors can provide higher magnetic fields, resulting in a significant reduction in the size of the reactor and thus in its cost. Less Tritium would also be needed. But large-scale production of HTS wires still requires more research and development.

Another possibility offered by the new superconductors is the construction of underground power lines capable of carrying power without loss over distances of more than 1,000 kilometers. Such lines may be necessary to bring power from remote renewable sources to areas where it is needed, for example, from offshore wind turbines or from photovoltaic panels installed in remote but very sunny desert areas.

3. Climate Repair

There are many ways to limit additional CO_2 emissions. We have mentioned some of them. But let us not forget that in the end the only way to repair the damage done to the climate is to eliminate the 100 ppm that have been added to the atmosphere during the last decades. This is because the level of 420 ppm already reached is beyond the value of about 300 ppm above which major changes such as the end of interglacial periodicity will take place. Melting of artic ice is projected within 100 years, and melting of the Greenland ice sheet is foreseen in about a 1,000 years, and this even if we immediately stop all additional CO_2 emissions.

The application of the notion of Entropy to the climate problem has allowed us to calculate how much energy is needed to eliminate the excess CO_2. Without this knowledge, we would be at a loss of calculating this energy. Entropy is not a matter of interest just to physicists. It touches here on a point essential for our survival on earth.

We have made a calculation of this energy and have shown that it is of the order of what 1,000 nuclear plants delivering each 1 GW could provide in 10 years. This energy could also be provided by any non-carbonate source. Both ways, or any combination of them, are feasible. Nuclear-electricity-delivered power is now about 450 GW. A similar power is delivered by solar and wind electricity. By using all this power to pump out CO_2 from the atmosphere, the excess could be eliminated in 10 years.

CO_2 capture has made some progress on a small scale. It is possible on a large scale. Storing the pumped CO_2 would also be necessary.

4. The Mistake to be Avoided

Unfortunately, very little money has been invested so far in the development of networks for the generation, transport, and use of low entropy, low CO_2 emission energy, and for the elimination of excess CO_2. Without massive investments in powerful innovative technologies, we will be condemned to more pollution and eventually to decay.

China's development exploited low nominal wages and cheap local fossil fuels, primarily coal. At the beginning, massive investments were made by rich countries that delocalized their industrial production. China got richer, its GDP per capita rose from a few hundred dollars to \$10,000. It is now the first industrial power in the world. Its contribution to the lowering of the price of solar energy has been decisive. It also dominates the market of lithium batteries for electric cars, and maybe soon the market of electric cars itself. These developments are positive for Chinese people and for the world. But China has also become the most polluting country in the world, now endangering our collective future.

India's development is following a similar path. It produces and consumes more, and is burning more coal, further deteriorating the climate.

Will Africa follow the same path as China and India? It might.

There is no lack of investors to develop Africa, as there was no lack of investors to develop China and then India. Africa too can offer a large market, cheap labor, and abundant natural resources. African countries might repeat the same kind of growth based on the massive use of coal and low wages. This would drive up CO_2 concentrations and climate disorder to new levels.

It is clear that the capital resources rich countries still have should rather be invested in the development of technologies that will allow emission free growth in Africa. To avoid repetition, the WTO should adopt new rules to prevent free capital movement for investments based primarily on local low nominal wages and cheap coal power. A better way is to help African countries develop a strong basis for CO_2-free energy growth. African latitudes are attractive for the massive use of solar electricity since the need for storage — particularly long-term seasonal storage — is much reduced. Energy cost in northern countries is going through the roof. The prospect of cheap energy available all year long that Africa can offer is in the long term more attractive for industry than low wages and cheap coal.

There is no shortage of innovation areas to explore. They require massive investments. This must be our priority if we want to maintain a reasonable and sustainable growth.

Appendix

Solar-Wind Duo, Nuclear Energy and Hydrogen as Options for the Future

Finding ways to replace fossil fuels by decarbonated energy sources is at the heart of current attempts to prevent further climate instabilities. In a recent book "Unsettled: What Climate Science Tells Us, What It Doesn't, and Why It Matters", Steven Koonin discusses various options, ranging from biofuels to solar and wind. After a careful review, he concludes that none of them can replace coal, oil and natural gas, because they are too expensive or suffer from basic deficiencies such as a variability that does not allow a continuous energy supply. He has also pointed out the sheer size of the challenge. Energy solutions must allow large-scale implementation because the high standard of living that we enjoy in developed countries has only been made possible by a massive use of energy. De-growth is not a serious option.

Steven Koonin reached his conclusions while he was Chief Scientist at British Petroleum. The task he had been given by BP was to select alternative energy technologies that were worth investing in. His answer to BP was: oil and gas. And he was right. It was in continuing to invest in oil and gas that BP and other similar companies made the most money. Indeed, oil remains so far the unique energy source for some critical needs such as transportation. Without oil, our economy would quickly collapse; cars and trucks, in many countries railways, sea transport of goods, air transportation would be paralyzed.

But the views on the climate that Koonin expressed at the same time drew considerable criticisms. He minimized the dangers of continuing to burn fossil fuels, going as far as saying that the global warning of one degree Celsius seen so far did not prevent us from living under the best conditions that humanity ever enjoyed, so why should an additional degree frighten us (Steven Koonin and Jordan Peterson, Youtube interview, January 16, 2023).

Koonin also expressed criticisms regarding renewables. *Inter alia*, he stressed that their variability and unpredictability does not allow replacement of fossil fuels in the absence of a massive energy storage solution. Interestingly enough, this criticism is similar to that made by proponents of nuclear energy. They also argue that solar and wind cannot replace energy sources that can be turned on and off at will. If fossil fuels are not anymore acceptable, what else they say is left besides nuclear energy? But if nuclear energy is banned, and alternative energy sources are impractical, is there any hope left?

The view on the climate that we have expressed in this book is somewhat different from that held by Koonin, and also to that of the proponents of nuclear energy. Our view is also different from the IPCC mainstream successive reports which have focused their attention primarily on global warming as the most serious threat.

It suffices to have a look at the evolution of the CO_2 concentration in the atmosphere to get convinced that the problem is more serious than Koonin would like us to believe, and more general than just global warming. In a matter of less than a century, it has increased to more than 420 ppm compared to the highest level on record for the last million years, which was 280 ppm. Such a rapid and massive increase has never occurred before. The biosphere is a complex system. As Koonin himself says, in complex systems small perturbations can have large effects. So how can one predict the effect of a sudden 50% increase in CO_2 concentration? How can one affirm that it will be small?

Focusing our attention on global warming may also be an error. I do not believe that we can predict all the consequences of such a massive and rapid increase in CO_2 concentration. Besides long-term global warming, more immediate threats such as massive droughts and floods may be more serious. While predictions regarding a continuing *global* warming are well established, those regarding *local* events are not. In the short term they may constitute the most dangerous threat. We just do not know.

This is why our aim should not be just to stop the increase in CO_2 concentration. One must go beyond the recommendations of the IPCC and *reverse* this increase on the time scale of one hundred years, for the reasons we have given in Chapter 8.

It is the purpose of this appendix to present two approaches that can provide de-carbonated energy on a large scale. Both are based on recent progress in energy generation.

These two approaches are very different. One of them, the solar-wind-hydrogen combination, has become attractive because of a recent massive cost reduction in photovoltaic modules that was not foreseen 20 years ago. The other, nuclear fusion, long considered an unreachable goal for this century, has now become feasible because of the recent discovery of stronger superconducting materials. Their application is quickly moving from the lab to industry, hopefully enabling to build fusion machines before the end of this century. Implemented on a large scale and combined with hydrogen production and distribution, both approaches would free us from our dependency on oil and gas, and allow cleaning up the atmosphere. In that sense, I am more optimistic than Koonin.

The solar-wind-hydrogen approach is based on proven technologies but will require a complete re-organization of energy distribution; the fusion approach still needs some additional steps before it can be implemented but will use the electricity energy distribution as we know it today for most uses.

There are of course other options. But these two are new and sufficiently attractive to make our point, namely that recent progress through research and development is the key to finding an acceptable solution.

1. Nuclear Fission Reactors

Now that damage caused by the massive use of fossil fuels has finally been recognized, nuclear energy is again receiving a more positive attention and the construction of additional fission reactors is seriously considered. This is a positive development. Fission reactors work well, but for reasons that we will now briefly review, it may not be possible to expand them sufficiently to satisfy energy needs on the scale of the planet.

1.1 *Limits to the expansion of fission reactors*

The currently used nuclear reactors burn fuel that consists of a mix of 2 uranium isotopes, U-235 and U-238. U-235 is unstable and can emit a neutron that, when captured by another U-235 atom, will trigger the emission of another neutron. If this event is sufficiently frequent a chain reaction can start. This is achieved if the U-235 concentration is of the order of 3 to 5%. Natural uranium contains only 0.7% of U-235. To turn it into a usable fuel one needs first to enrich it. Only a few countries can do that, but this is not what has limited the extension of fission reactors so far.

What has prevented it is the insufficient availability of natural uranium. Proven reserves, according to the IAEA, amount to about 1.10^7 tons, while the yearly need to supply existing fission reactors is of about 1.10^5 tons. Proven reserves can only provide fuel to existing reactors, and for about 100 to 200 years. These are rough numbers. More uranium can certainly be discovered, but not to the amount needed to allow a general use of fission reactors around the world.

There are less than 20 countries that produce a significant amount of nuclear electricity. There is no African and no South African country in that list (see Figure A1).

After a fast increase in the 1970s, the world production of nuclear electricity has stabilized at a level of about 2,500 TWh per year (see Figure A2). This is about 10% of the world electricity production, but in some countries such as France it is much more than 10%. There are about 450 nuclear power plants around the world. Production from South America and Africa is too small to be visible on that graph.

1.2. *Breeder reactors*

The limited resources in natural uranium have prompted nuclear scientists in countries massively using nuclear electricity to develop a different kind

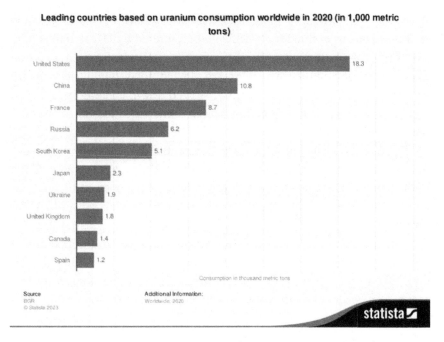

Figure A1.   Total world uranium consumption is of the order of 50,000 tons per year. World reserves are currently estimated to be around 8 million tons.

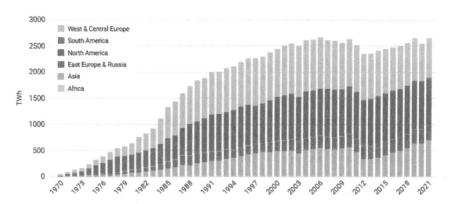

Figure A2.   World production of nuclear electricity since 1970. Most of it is produced in West and Central Europe, North America and Asia (mostly Japan). East Europe and Russia also contribute.

of reactor that produces more fuel than it consumes. This is possible because neutrons emitted by U-235 can be captured by U-238 that is then transformed into Plutonium Pu 239, itself a fissile isotope. In a fission reactor, neutrons emitted by U-235 are slowed down to enhance capture by another U-235. If neutrons are not slowed down, capture by U-238 is enhanced. This is what is done in a breeder reactor, called for this reason fast neutron reactor.

In spite of many difficult technical problems fast neutron breeder reactors were eventually developed successfully in France and in the Soviet Union. The French reactor Superphenix developed in France was connected to the grid. In 1996 it reached 90% of the planned 1,242 MWe output.

Yet, in 1998 the French government under Lionel Jospin decided to close down Superphenix. This was a political rather than a technical decision, taken under pressure from the Green Party. In the long term this decision, if accepted worldwide, may limit the use of fission reactors to a small number of countries for a limited amount of time. China, however, has still plans for building fast neutron breeder reactors, with the goal of producing 1,400 GW of electricity by 2100.

1.3. *Nuclear and CO_2 waste*

Pressure from the green parties in France and other countries to stop the development of nuclear energy was motivated in large part by the problem of radioactive waste disposal. Decisions to slow down (France) or to close down completely (Germany) nuclear electricity plants were taken at a time where the climate issue only started to emerge.

What was not understood at that time was that the CO_2 accumulating in the atmosphere because of fossil fuel burning was itself a dangerous waste, at least as dangerous as radioactive waste. Stopping the development of nuclear electricity amounted to burning more fossil fuel. CO_2 spread all over the planet and put at risk all populations, whether they burned large amounts of fossil fuels or not. Instead, radioactive waste is buried in countries enjoying the nuclear energy supply. While the green parties claimed that the purpose of their fight against nuclear electricity was to protect the environment, their success achieved exactly the opposite result. The spread of CO_2 from fuel burning is like garbage thrown all over the planet without any control. No one cares about collecting it, and in fact no one knows exactly how this could be done. Green parties that were so active in alerting against the dangers of nuclear waste did not alert against the dangers of CO_2 waste.

We are all today much more at risk than if we had pursued the development of nuclear electricity through breeder reactors. It is quite possible that this option will never be revived. China has not abandoned it. Much depends on what she decides to do.

2. The Solar-Wind-Hydrogen Combination

Photovoltaic solar cells use semiconductors such as crystalline Silicium (Silicon) to convert the energy of photons emitted by the Sun into electrical energy. This is achieved by implanting a junction to produce an electric field near the surface of the crystal. Energy provided by incoming photons allow electrons to be released from the atoms they belong to. They are accelerated by this field, creating a voltage drop across the semiconductor crystal, making it an electrical power source.

Solar cells are a by-product of the invention of the transistor by John Bardeen, William Shockley and Walter Brattain shortly after World War 2. Solar cells are made with the same semiconductor and the same kind of junctions as in the transistor. In the 1960s photovoltaic (PV) cells became of interest as power sources for satellites, because of their small specific weight and the almost 24 hours availability of solar radiation in space. The high cost of PV cells was not an impediment for space application. But a terrestrial application was not considered because the high PV cost, of several US$100/Watt, which was prohibitive. In any case there was no shortage of energy as oil was cheap and abundant.

A drastic change of expectations occurred in the early 1970s, when Arab states imposed on the USA and other countries an oil embargo because of their support to Israel during the Yom Kippur War.

The USA as well as European countries and Japan had grown increasingly dependent on Arab oil. The embargo prompted them to look for ways to diversify their energy resources. The rapid development of nuclear energy in the 1970s (see Figure A2) was one of the outcomes of the oil embargo, particularly for European countries that had no oil resources of their own. PV terrestrial applications also started to receive some attention, particularly in the USA. But the challenge was formidable, as a cost reduction by orders of magnitude was necessary for large scale terrestrial PV use.

2.1. *An unexpected massive PV cost reduction*

Alternatives to the use of crystalline silicon were considered; growing crystals is a slow process. Cells based on amorphous silicon and several polycrystalline composites were tested successfully but their conversion efficiency was limited. In the end crystalline silicon cells won out. Massive and continuous investments were made in China. It is amazing to see what industry can do in terms of cost reduction (see Figure A3).

The cost of the individual cells is now a negligible fraction of the cost of PV module, and, *a fortiori,* of PV installations comprising many such modules. The cost reduction of solar cells, going from more than US$100/ Watt in the early 1970s to less than US$1/Watt today, has triggered an exponential rise of the delivered solar electricity on a world scale (see Figure A4). Negligible until 2010, it kicked off when the cost fell below a few US$/Watt. A further and massive cost reduction occurred with the large-scale use of PV. In 2022 PV power production crossed the level of 1,000 TWh. Solar modules and wind turbines together deliver today more energy than that delivered by all the nuclear power plants: 2,500 TWh (see Figure A2).

Solar and wind electricity has thus passed the crucial test of scale.

2.2. *The future impact of solar and wind electricity*

The cost of electricity produced by wind turbines has also decreased, though not as much as the cost of PV electricity (see Figure A5).

The rapid expansion of solar and wind electricity is in sharp contrast with the stagnation of nuclear electricity. PV modules are building blocks that can deliver electrical power to individual homes as well as to medium size communities. Their use is universal. Of course, areas having abundant sunshine will allow more power to be delivered on a yearly basis, but

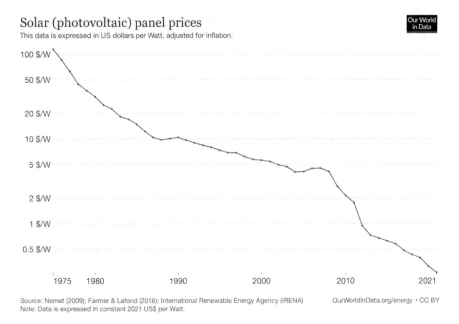

Figure A3. Evolution of the production cost of crystalline Silicium PV cells.

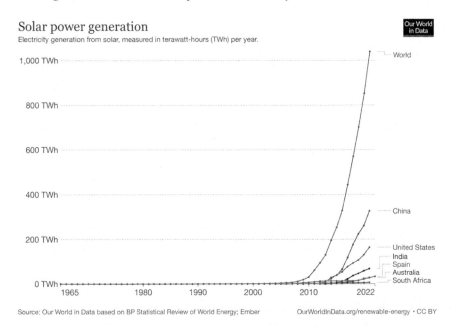

Figure A4. Negligible until 2010, the power generated by PV modules is now increasing exponentially thanks to a massive cost reduction in the fabrication of solar cells.

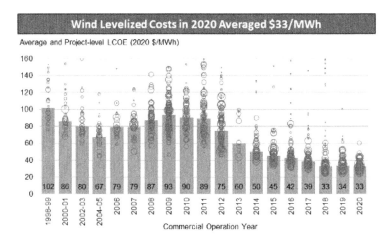

Figure A5.   Evolution of the production cost of wind electricity since the early 2000s. It has decreased but now seems to have stabilized around US$0.033/kWh. This is not the cost paid by the customer, about US$0.20/kWh in the USA. By comparison, a home PV installation in the US delivers electricity at a cost of US$0.06 to US$0.08/kWh.

today solar electricity can be competitive almost anywhere. The sun shines unevenly, but it shines everywhere.

The impact of solar and wind electricity can go beyond replacing existing power sources. As of now electrical energy represents only around 15% to 20% of the total power consumed in most countries. Household and transportation consume together almost two thirds of our total energy. They still use mostly fossil fuels.

Because PV is already economical on the individual house scale, it has the potential to change this dependency. A roof area is sufficient to deliver enough electrical power used by households, and at the same time the energy needed for an electrical individual vehicle. At the same time the car battery can be used for electricity storage.

The low-cost production of solar cells also allows a competitive production of hydrogen by electrolysis. Hydrogen is now considered as a replacement of natural gas for industry, and as an alternative fuel for electrical vehicles.

Distribution of hydrogen is more delicate than that of oil and electricity because of safety considerations. Large scale implementation of a solar-wind-hydrogen combination is extremely attractive. It has a potential that we could not imagine 20 years ago. The PV massive cost reduction, and that of wind turbines, was hoped for by people working in the field for many years. Still, when it finally occurred, it was a surprise for many knowledgeable people. Its long-term overall consequences will take time to develop.

3. The New Nuclear Fusion Option

Controlling fusion on earth has been the dream of physicists since the fifties. The fuel — hydrogen — is in abundant supply. Fusion of two hydrogen atoms to produce a helium atom releases an amount of energy equal to the mass lost in this fusion. This is what happens in the sun and provides us with the solar radiation from which we live.

This is for the principle. In practice the Deuterium and Tritium isotopes of Hydrogen are used. The D-T reaction releases 17.5 MeV of energy and a neutron. Deuterium is in ample supply (1/5000 of sea water). Tritium is not, but it can be regenerated in the reactor by using a Lithium blanket, which when submitted to neutron radiation produces Tritium.

The so far unsolved problem has been to get the D-T atoms close enough to each other, and for a long enough time, for fusion to take place. They need to get enough kinetic energy for this to happen, which requires heating the gas up to a very high temperature. At high temperatures atoms release their electron, the gas becomes a plasma of positive ions and negative electrons.

This plasma is unstable; it needs active containment for the fusion reaction to take place. This is achieved in Tokamak reactors where a strong magnetic field provided by superconducting coils traps the plasma in a torus. The higher the field, the smaller the torus can be.

3.1. *The ITER project*

The maximum field value produced by superconducting coils is limited to a fraction of their critical field. Coils made of the superconducting alloy used in MRI scanners — NbTi — can only produce fields of up to about 3 Tesla in large volumes. This is insufficient for a Tokamak fusion machine, which requires a field of at least 10 Tesla to keep the size of the

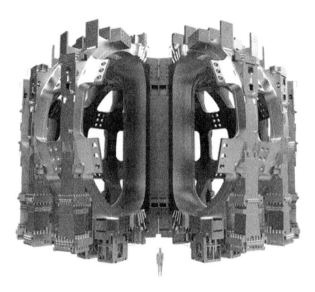

Figure A6.   The ITER Tokamak.

Tokamak machine down to an acceptable value. Just as a reminder, a field of 10 Tesla is a million times larger than the Earth's magnetic field.

The superconductor used In the ITER machine — Nb_3Sn — is more advanced than that used in MRI machines. it can sustain higher fields because it has a higher critical field of more than 20 Tesla. 18 toroidal coils made from that alloy have been produced for the ITER project. They are impressive: 19 meters high, 9 meters wide. They surround the torus, each encased in a cryostat maintained at a temperature a few degrees above absolute zero, or about 271 degrees Celsius (see Figure A6).

First Plasma is scheduled to take place in 2025, and the D-T first fusion reaction for 2035. Delays are probable.

3.2. *Beyond ITER with the new superconductors*

As can be seen, the ITER machine is very large. More than 30 countries participate in the project. It will produce energy (500 MW) but its main purpose is to be a substantial step towards the later fabrication of a prototype fusion power reactor.

In the meantime new superconductors were discovered. In 1986 Bednorz and Muller discovered a new family of ceramic materials that become superconducting at a higher temperature; typically around 100 K for the compound $YBa_2Cu_3O_7$ instead of about 20K for Nb_3 Sn. They also have higher critical fields: 100 Tesla instead of 20 Tesla. The combination of a higher critical temperature and higher critical field makes them very attractive for Tokamak fusion machines.

One difficult problem was to produce them in wire form. This was a difficult task because they ceramic materials are brittle. It took more than 30 years to achieve this goal. The solution found was to grow them in the form of thin films, a few micron thick, deposited on a flexible metallic substrate. One example of this realization is shown Figure A7.

The wire remains fully superconducting up to a current of 1,000 A/ mm^2 at a temperature of 20K and under a magnetic field of 20T. The higher critical field allows a large reduction in the size of the machine compared to that of the ITER, by about a factor of 10, and the higher temperature reduces the cost and complexity of cooling. These advantages should shorten the path towards the commercialization of fusion machines, from a century to a few decades.

The first large scale magnet of this kind was successfully tested in 2021. The SPARC MIT-Commonwealth Fusion project will use 18 similar

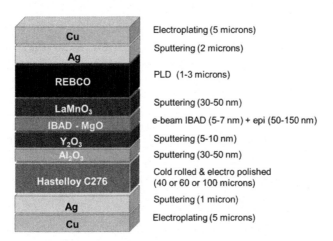

Figure A7. A high temperature ceramic superconductor composed of a rare earth RE (like Y), Barium Ba, Copper Cu and oxygen O, a few micron thick, is grown at high temperature on a metallic Hastealloy ribbon. Several very thin buffer layers are grown in between to prevent unwanted diffusion and maintain high crystalline quality (after A. Molodyk *et al.*, Nature Scientific Reports, 11:2084 (2011)).

toroidal field magnets, the same number as in the ITER project. But the ITER coils comprise 100,000 km, about 20 times more, of the less advanced Nb_3Sn superconductor, giving only a field of 12T.

The SPARC project is relatively recent and is much less advanced than ITER, whose coils have already been fabricated. But it holds the potential to move faster and to be more flexible for possible modifications because of its smaller size and related smaller cost.

Table A1 shows the progress accomplished towards the application of superconducting wires to fusion machines. A minimum engineering critical current density of about 1,000 A/mm^2 is required for fusion toroidal coils. At a temperature of 4 Kelvin this value is achieved only up to 6 Tesla for NbTi wire. This is insufficient. Development of the more advanced Nb_3Sn superconductor has allowed the construction of ITER operating at 12 Tesla at 4 degrees Kelvin. The SPARC fusion machine is based on the more advanced toroidal coils using REBCO wire. They will provide a field of 20 Tesla at a temperature of 20 degrees Kelvin. They will also be smaller, their refrigeration costs will be lower and the stability should be improved because of the higher temperature.

Progress in the development of stronger superconductors has thus been critical to make controlled fusion an achievable commercial goal. Note that more than 30 years of intense research have been needed to turn the discovered ceramic superconductors into practical wires and coils. A similar time scale can be expected before fusion machine will become commercially available.

Table A1

	NbTi	**Nb3Sn**	**REBCO**
Year of discovery	1961	1961	1986
Critical temperature	9 degrees Kelvin	18 degrees Kelvin	90 degrees Kelvin
Critical field	9 Tesla	30 Tesla	100 Tesla
1,000 A/mm^2 engineering critical current	At 4 degrees Kelvin 6 Tesla	At 4 degrees Kelvin 15 Tesla	At 20 degrees Kelvin 20 Tesla
Tokamak Fusion	No	Yes, ITER	Yes, SPARC
Power fusion reactor	No	Doubtful	Possible

Index

Printed in Great Britain
by Amazon

56335990R00096